VEHICLE IN COLLISION:
what did *you* see ?

Godfrey Holmes

NETHERMOOR BOOKS

© **Godfrey Holmes**
Cover & all line Illustrations
by Anna Maria Dutto

February 2016

ISBN : 978-0-9536016-9-1

NETHERMOOR BOOKS
"St. Elphin"
12 North Promenade
Withernsea
Kingston-upon-Hull
East Riding of Yorkshire
HU19 2DP
Telephone : 01964-615258

Contact the Author :
godfrey.holmes@btinternet.com

Whilst every effort has been made to stay faithful to laws operating in England & Wales at the end of 2015, and to observe the Highway Code, the Author presents these 100 (representative) scenarios for thought-provoking purposes only. There will be times or places where a junction or highway will not be laid out exactly as illustrated. So it is wise not to use this book, by itself, in any vehicle insurance claim or court case.

CONTENTS :

✥ DEDICATED TO THE MEMORY ✥
OF MY COLLEGE ROOM-MATE :
KILLED IN THE 1967
"COMEX" COACH CRASH ;
ALSO TO THE MEMORY
OF THE 16-YEAR OLD GIRL
WHO LIVED OPPOSITE ME:
KILLED IN A HEAD-ON COLLISION
ONE SUNDAY AFTERNOON
IN JUNE 2008 ;
FINALLY TO THE MEMORY OF ALL
THOSE MEN & WOMEN -
WHOSE NAMES I SHALL NEVER
KNOW - KILLED ON DIFFERENT
ROADS JUST MINUTES
AHEAD OF ME

✥   ✥

INTRODUCTION :

How do we know we have actually seen what we think we have seen? We need somebody to pinch us and say : " Yes : that sounds right!" Another set of eyes. Another perspective. Another spectator's enclosure.

Never is being a witness more important than in the event of a collision on the road. *Collision*, not accident - because "accidents" would have to be unavoidable , or at least unforeseeable, by at least one of the parties implicated. And with most road collisions : up to 95%, being *accidental* does not enter the equation. The notion of *fault* comes into play alongside fate.

And we, as a society, are rather uncomfortable with fault : mainly because it's bound up with blame, possible guilt too. Moreover it's far more likely to have been *somebody else's* fault, not my fault ; and fault comes out as rather expensive . People want compensating for fault- at the very least, they want full repayment of any disbursements and loss of earnings - which, in the case of damaged vehicles, delays, flattened bollards, whiplash, can amount to thousands. *Worse*, fault might be criminal. That means Police, Courts, the DVLA and so-called small claims. So it is in nearly everybody's interest for any driver to keep his or her own counsel.

Beyond contest, road crashes are an enormous social and medical problem: one of the biggest killers; with suicide, the biggest source of injury to everyone aged 15 to 50. And however low the Government sets its target for bringing down needless deaths and injuries, the only logical target is NIL! Young or old, driver or non-driver, bus operator or bus passenger, courier or customer, we must have zero tolerance towards road crashes and the human stresses or deficits, combined with mechanical breakdowns, that lead to those collisions: vehicle with vehicle, vehicle with person, cyclist with motorcyclist.

The reason this subject is neglected - and the dreadful phenomenon of death and injury skated over - is the ubiquity of the auto-mobile : literally that means of locomotion, that "freedom of the road," that we all yearn for, or are programmed so to desire.

Therefore police, nurses, paramedics, road-menders, magistrates, even passer-by, develop too great a tolerance of the devastation surrounding vehicles in collision; taking almost for granted not only shattered glass and shattered plans, but also *shattered lives*. If we treated the car as a gun - or as an unguarded factory machine - there would be public outcry. Similarly, if all the deaths and injuries happened *within one week*, rather than spread over 52 weeks, there would be mass protests. And the Prime Minister would stumble over Petitions.

In the first 60 of 100 Scenarios outlined below, I am not asking the reader to work out *exactly* what took place, down to the last shaft of sunlight or stray cat. Instead, I am challenging readers, and whoever will re-enact or re-run collisions which have already taken place, to work out where different persons are standing or sitting.

Inevitably, the Author himself is here sharing his own testimony, real or created: partly because it is usually impossible, or bad practice, for strangers on the scene to photograph an actual collision; partly because most witnesses do not stay rooted to the spot, and might not be able to share their ideas till next week, next service station, or till the next breakdown truck has been called.

Certainly, anybody lucky, or unlucky, enough to have driven for 40 years has already seen too much, or heard too much from friends and relatives concerning what they have witnessed, worse, caused. Arguably, nobody ever gets over their nightmare on the highway.

Sometimes I do give the reader prompts or extra clues. Twenty times I ask the reader to allocate actual "fault." *Vehicle in Collision* is, without doubt, not the last word on the vital topic of being a Witness / participant / injured party, whilst acting as driver, passenger or pedestrian - but I know it is the first attempt *to work within this particular format.* And where *one* traveller embarks on a journey, somebody soon follows! G.H.H.

A NOTE ABOUT TRUTH AND LYING

Students delight in speculating: << If you are a villain claiming that all your co-defendants are lying, *are you yourself fibbing*? >>

The first eighty of one hundred Scenarios illustrated below rely on *good faith.*

Were any, or all, of the witnesses quoted *not* telling the truth as they understood it, the Reader would go beyond simply double-guessing the Author [having due regard to clues and illustrations provided]- to double-guessing those witnesses also. Allowing no meaningful solution!

Therefore, Author and Reader alike must take the first 80+ witness statements, *or groups of witness statements*, at face value. *My* witnesses do want to tell the truth to whoever will listen: family, friend, or police constable. After all, it is not *they* who have to settle up with Insurance, Highways, aggrieved third parties or the workplace. Impartial witnesses see the importance of staying detached whilst still being of assistance.

That said, Scenarios 81 to 100 inclusive *actually depend on* an element of truth or untruth. Here, the Reader is encouraged to cast doubt on everyone's testimony, with some notable exceptions. That is why so many staff training days include role-play. Most role play is safe.

The difference in emphasis here is deliberate: because the first and main witnesses in Collisions 81 to 100 *are actual participants*. And participants in Vehicle Collision are rightly or wrongly assumed to be partisan; biased; more fearful of repercussions; self-serving.

But *even here*, there are instances of recovered memory - also understandable confusion. If a participant is guilty of *accidental* misrepresentation, it is often because he or she is too close to the event, too aware of amazing circumstances, too familiar with tragic outcome; too knocked sideways: *literally!* Most of these survivors, hesitant or bold, patient or exasperated, are not acting *out of malice* ; less so, intent on defrauding their Insurance Companies, or perverting the course of justice.

So, again, it would be nonsense if *everybody* leaving scenes 81 to 100 was fibbing - although in real life there certainly are crashes where every single person involved stays loyal to the less probable - *less possible* - version of what has happened. Here, at least, *somebody* is telling the truth! Until judge or juror, solicitor or barrister comes to the conclusion that they are not.

ΩΨΩΨΩΨΩΨΩΨΩ

ONE HUNDRED CRASH OR COLLISION SCENARIOS
& how to solve them

Scenarios one to sixty :

here, all you need do is match up the
six Witnesses quoted to their six positions
on or near the road concerned:
eg. 1(C) ; 2(D) ; 3(F) ; 4(A) ; 5(B) ; & 6(E) ;
.....and remember : *none* of these witnesses
giving testimony are drivers of a vehicle in collision;
nor is any witness a passenger in one of the vehicles
implicated; nor is any voice you hear that of
an immediate victim / survivor *

Scenarios sixty-extra to eighty :

here, please weigh up all the many witness
statements / memories and give yourself marks for
determining, *as nearly as possible*, what was
the collision that took place on that road, that day?
here, you are also asked to answer: Whose Fault ? *

Scenarios eighty-one to one hundred :

here, read what each actual driver or passenger has
to say after their collision - and establish which very
special witness or witnesses can be relied upon ? *

* all Solutions are given on Page Nos. 123 - 124

COLLISION ONE :

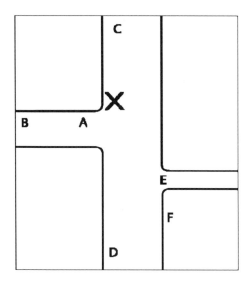

1) " I remember walking down the hill and seeing a real build-up of traffic at the staggered junction. The moped had passed me okay...."

2) " I'd waited, no luck. That black Taxi almost screeched Left ...."

3) " I think the up-and-down traffic was relentless. Side roads would just have to wait : maybe 7 minutes or more...."

4) " When I passed, a Taxi was honking to get round and out...."

5) " We *all* had to wait. It was rush hour. What I objected to was that same Taxi racing past me and the parked Bus 200 yards back..."

6) " I pity the poor lady driver. She looked so nervous trying to turn Right. She should have gone Left. Now she'll think it's *her* fault..."

COLLISION TWO :

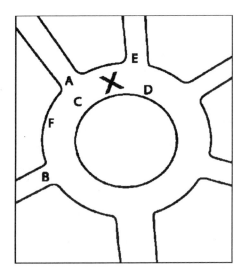

1) "My view was rather restricted - and people were joining or leaving the Roundabout all the time - but the white van seemed to be trying to find his Left exit at the very moment a car was blind-side."

2) "I think a lot of drivers were over-committed - and faster than they should have. I saw an almost inevitable collision back of me."

3) " I put my Left indicator on proper early - cos it's not that easy to gain Left against traffic-flow. I blame speedy joiners!"

4) " I could have waited ages for my inside lane : almost round the clock-face. From what I observed, white van man was on phone."

5) " As I walked across, 2 vehicles ahead were on collision course."

6) " No, the white van had no Left indicator - nor really the other man - unless it came on late. Both drivers unsure till too late!"

COLLISION THREE :

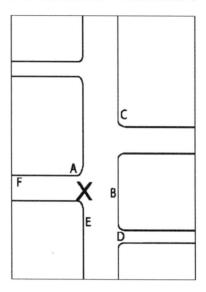

1) " Both of them were at fault. One was poking out, the other swerving in - and they both moved at exactly the same moment."

2) " As I prepared to cross, I noticed an Ambulance with no blue lights pass me and swing Right into that particular turning."

3) " I suppose I was in the best position of all : right where I could see this Chelsea Tractor well out for its Right turn, glanced by this Ambulance - which in fairness *was* cutting the corner...."

4) "By my going a bit slower, just in case something came out in front of me, I was giving the Ambulance permission to go for it!"

5) "When I've come down here before, cars tend to stay a bit Left rather than stick out. I think his vision might have been obstructed."

6) " They both had the same trajectory, I suggest. Must be 50-50!"

COLLISION FOUR :

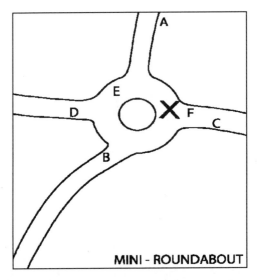

MINI - ROUNDABOUT

1) " Yes, that turning-circle is rather tight. But the road was ice-free, and with a little less haste, this long lorry could have made it..."

2) " I knew by how things were shaping that there would be trouble if the tractor-unit turned too quickly. Could have been me on skids!"

3) " The jack-knife was just happening as I got there, so, very wisely, I stopped exactly where I was, waiting developments..."

4) " Yes, it was slippery underfoot, so early in the day. When I saw the commotion, I knew things were really bad. The car wedged beneath the trailer unit might have been a bit too near...."

5) " I'd just passed the lorry driver - who shouldn't really have been on there. It had been an awfully cold and moonlit night."

6) " I caught a view of the truck driver leaping out of his skewed cab. He looked totally unharmed, unlike the other driver...."

14

COLLISION FIVE :

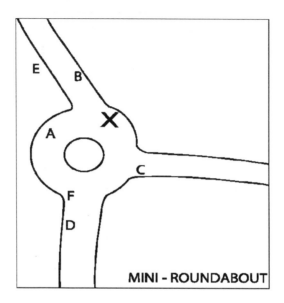

MINI - ROUNDABOUT

1) " Waiting to cross, I could hear that awful crunch where I could not really cross safely at this time of day."

2) " I was surprised that anybody would enter this Roundabout without looking. I don't think he wanted to change down gear!"

3) " I was the one actually waiting for Speedy Gonzales to get out of the way. Not so speedy now!"

4) " At first I wondered why this car was not entering the fray..."

5) " By chance, I saw it all. The Jag was set on getting round first."

6) " The Jag was certainly in a hurry - and I didn't notice him braking at all. Effortless superiority. Only.... someone else pays!"

COLLISION SIX :

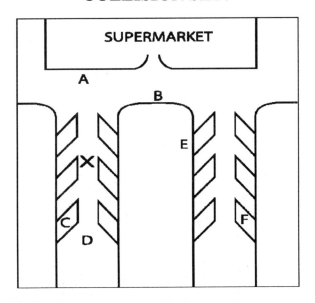

1) " I had just put my trolley back when I saw 2 cars reversing at exactly the same moment. Collision was inevitable!"

2) "It was a busy Friday teatime and I was waiting for Gladys to come out with the shopping when I heard this mighty thud...."

3) " I'd finished my shopping and was waiting to reverse out, but over my shoulder, I thought it better to wait a minute or to do."

4) " I suppose I had the best view of all. I don't think either driver cared in the least that they might not have a clear gangway!"

5) " I'd got a few bottles for recycling. I remember wondering why one - perhaps both - of the drivers reversed so fearlessly !"

6) " As back passenger, I had some notion of what was happening. I think I was curious! I'd always thought Superstores spelt danger."

16

COLLISION SEVEN :

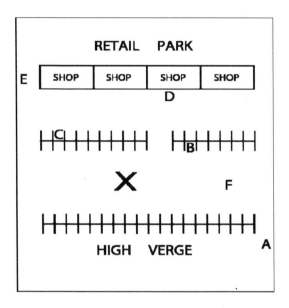

1) " This jeep - with about 6 people in it - came out back first, without looking, clean over this bloke. Chap stood no chance!"

2) " I thought I'd try some different stores. Wish I hadn't! I'll never forget this customer's cry of agony. And all the screaming."

3) " I'd just come out, and thought where's my car? Then I noticed this big black Range Rover stopped, with all its doors open..."

4) " I'd parked up and searched for my handbag. Through a bit of a gap, I saw this Mum rushing to lock up and get away. Oh dear!"

5) " Unusually, I was facing forward and saw the victim striding..."

6) " I'm not much help, and the sun was in my eyes, and I'd got other worries. But I remember how full this carrier was - and quick."

COLLISION EIGHT :

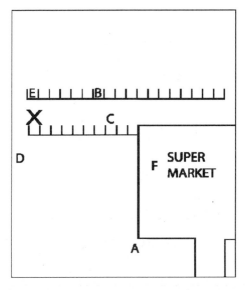

1) " It was chucking down with rain - and no way was this small van going to wait the lady preparing to head for the petrol pump."

2) " I was about to do that same turn, and I don't think the woman was reckless - not on this occasion."

3) " I'd not done my shopping yet. There were two workers in the front of the van - and no night watchman to see them out."

4) " I'm lazy and had gone in forward. Also I wanted to go alongside the main store. About to reverse, I could see bad trouble."

5) " I was walking in a car lane, like you do. And I just got the impression she'd forgotten some stuff, because she was free to go."

6) " I'm a bit nosy. Through the glass, this workman eating his pasty was still heading backwards. Crunch!"

18

COLLISION NINE :

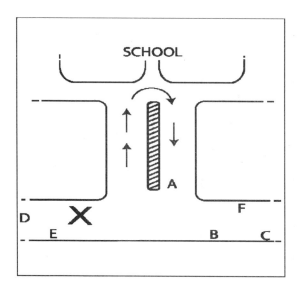

1) " I only saw him coming off in my rear mirror - but I knew he was riding safely and steadily."

2) " What a pity the lad had to pass so many parked cars ahead. I'd parked a bit lazily, but at least on the Left side. And it was wet."

3) " I was wanting that Left lane as she did - but safer.. I could see what was going to happen , immediately I saw her car set off."

4) " I'd just collected my two - as she had. But, crucially, I was facing straight on. I do hope she saw I hadn't nodded her to go!"

5) " There was a lot happening : in pouring rain. The bike looked okay - and had his light on. I don't think the green car did..."

6) " I was still parked up. She must have had so many blind spots! I was both astonished and horrified when I saw what she was doing."

COLLISION TEN :

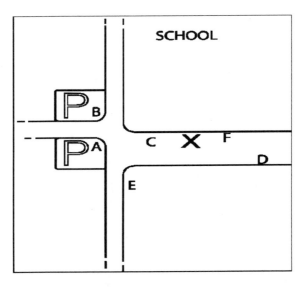

1) " I think this Grand-dad - looked the age of a Grand-dad - was giving way to some children like me : hurrying to cross."

2) " My job as Dinner Lady was to shut the gate when the last kiddie was in class. This man's car was really shunted forward."

3) "A few seconds later and I'd have known how much notice this teenage driver was given : perhaps none."

4) " I'd taken a little bit longer to park up. There seemed to be parents everywhere : some parked, some driving, some gossiping."

5) " I'm amazed there aren't more shunts. Excited kids do run."

6) " I insist on walking my boy and his best mate to school. So many parents and grandparents leave it too late at 9 o'clock, then arrive too early at 3pm - to bag a space! I heard metal on metal!"

COLLISION ELEVEN :

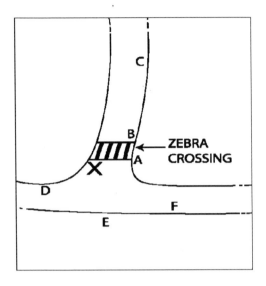

1) " I can't say I saw what the fuss was about. Nobody looked hurt ahead. Then I saw this 12-year old girl wailing!"

2) " I would have turned Right just after him. I think he thought the Zebra was clear."

3) " The dog was on a long lead. I have no doubt the driver who ran over the dog didn't see there was anything else crossing..."

4) " The little girl had already finished crossing. The trouble seemed to be her dog had so many interesting smells to sniff."

5) " From what I could see, the little girl was so glad to meet her mate at the other side that she forgot winding in her lead."

6) " When I crossed a moment or two before, I passed the girl plus dog. And I must say, I thought that driver was getting a bit ratty!"

COLLISION TWELVE :

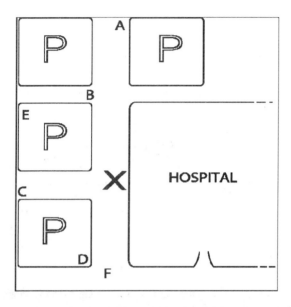

1) " It's terrible: just before 10 am. clinics. Everybody's fighting for the very few spaces. But it was *a Nurse* passing me before impact."

2) " I was walking briskly but turned to see the commotion!"

3) " I'd parked in about the last spot. Very foolishly some disappointed punters, like this disabled driver, did a U turn."

4) " I think the disabled driver could see no space and went, in despair, for the four car parks the other side of the Hospital."

5) " I'd failed to find a place as well, but had a bit more time. I don't think the nurse was on the phone, just adjusting her cap."

6) " I'd dropped off my wife already, and standing by my door. The Nurse might not have expected the swing. No reason to."

COLLISION THIRTEEN :

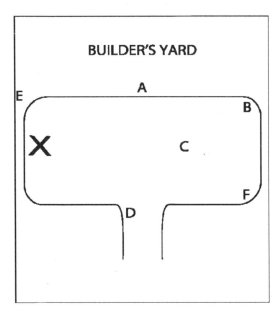

1) " Builders and vans were everywhere! This particular paint truck was boxed in - and hadn't got lookout. He reversed carelessly....."

2) " I'd got my back to the crash - but turned to see this woman passenger really distressed. She was still awaiting her hubbie."

3) " I was putting all the pipes in the back of my Transit when I heard two or three other builders yelling at the paint man to stop."

4) " Maybe the driver didn't realise a later parker had slipped in.... He certainly didn't look as if he thought he was so short of space.."

5) " I was ready for off and revving. The lorry's angle was odd!"

6) " I'd come away from paying. This bloke was yelling: NO! NO!"

COLLISION FOURTEEN :

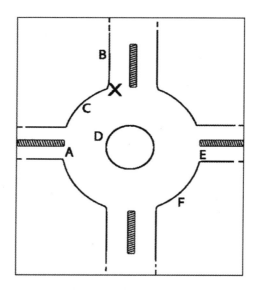

1) " I came out of the convenience store and noticed that the red Mini was running out of space. Maybe she hadn't seen the Coach?"

2) " I wasn't far off the red Mini - and she was clearly signalling Left - but unseen by the Coach driver high above her."

3) " I was just wondering how I'd walk across such a busy entry-road when I noted a long-distance Coach needing to make up time."

4) " The Roundabout was everso busy. I think all traffic was switching lane! The Coach had entered in his Right lane for forward.

5) " As I prepared for my Left, I almost had stall to creep behind the Coach hugging the very middle."

6) " I think I was trying to do the same : to exit straight from middle of Roundabout to Left exit. The line a long Coach follows is odd."

COLLISION FIFTEEN :

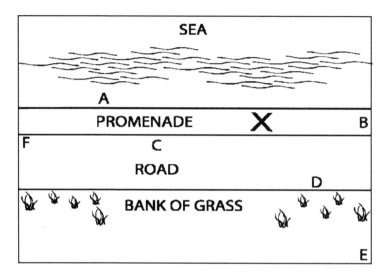

1) "As I approached the double-decker, the driver looked dazed and mounted his kerb. Seemed to plough through a long picnic bench."

2) " As I followed the Bus, it jerked first to the Right, then to the Left - which was when I could see the full impact."

3) " I'd only left my Hotel a few seconds earlier. On the far side of the road, I guess a Bus behind schedule rushed it and lost control."

4) "Drying myself and wrapped in a big towel, I saw this blue Bus somewhere it shouldn't have been. There was a lot of noise & screaming! Thank Goodness picnickers had chance to run!"

5) " The Bus well ahead of me was very full and driven very urgently...Then I got distracted seeing everyone yell and scatter."

6) " I'd just finished my sandwiches and I was looking for a rubbish bin for the wrappings. Good job I wasn't napping! What a sight!"

COLLISION SIXTEEN :

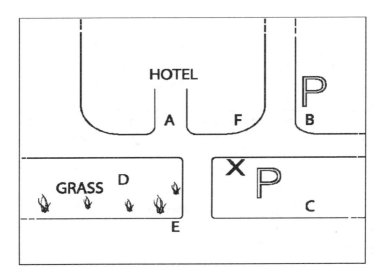

1) "It was a dark evening - yet only 5 o'clock: arrival time. I was just having Tea and looking out the window. What a commotion!"

2) " I'm so thankful I chose a different Car Park. I suppose I was getting my suitcase out as well : busy Friday! First I knew was a woman's - the mother's? - piercing scream : to S-T-O-P!"

3) " I'd arrived on bargain break an hour early, and gone out to buy sandwiches : don't tell Management! The car was reversing very slowly- but not enough to save the driver's daughter. If only...!"

4) " I'd just taken the dog for a wee - but was amazed how many tries this man was making to get into too narrow a chosen space."

5) " Just leaving! Bedlam! I wondered whether to help jack it up?"

6) " I was too close! I *saw* the little girl run to Mum wrong way!"

COLLISION SEVENTEEN :

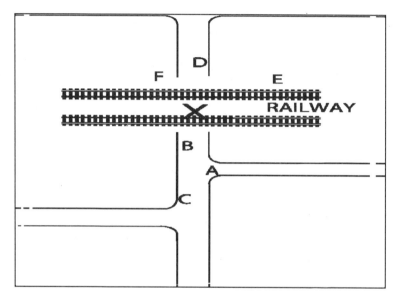

1) " I was just leaving the Station Car Park when I looked and saw - to my horror - this car the wrong side of the barrier, and yells!"

2) " I came to a halt too soon really. 'Cos I was amazed at what this Loony was trying to do: speed through on flashing red. Impossible!"

3) " Like all foot soldiers, I had to wait for the train too. We all knew the train would come too soon. Good job he leapt out!"

4) " They always say : 'Get a Grandstand seat!' Well I did! From some way off I'd noted down this geezer rushing to beat the wait..."

5) " I would have been waiting patiently -cept I was more anxious this fella got out allowed before the day of reck'ning. And he did!"

6) " I'd just bought my ticket when I saw a car on the line - then Wham! The car's wreckage was well-scattered - train halted!"

COLLISION EIGHTEEN :

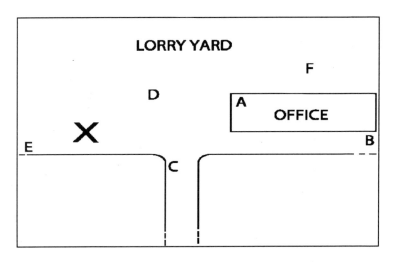

1) " I was lucky - wrong word, sorry! - to see how it happened. As one pipe slipped, another did: falling one by one on the poor driver."

2) " I was just waiting to drive up to their office, and park, when I noticed this man struggling to tighten the ropes. Then the clatter!"

3) " Lots of vehicles in the way, but they called me to do some heavy lifting...It needed more than me to raise those pipes."

4) " I wasn't doing more than look out of the window at that moment. Pipes were dropping everywhere, an onto white van man!"

5) " I was back in my cab ready to leave. My first impression was that it was a big job for one man to re-balance his load. Poor sod!"

6) " At first I thought I was clear! Then this dirty great 30foot pipe dislodged itself and swung round to squash my bonnet - and him!"

COLLISION NINETEEN :

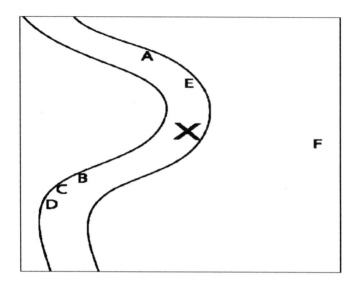

1) " Thank God I'd reason to hold back. It was awful to witness this motorbike misjudge the roundness of the bend - and be thrown off."

2) "At the end of the Footpath, I could see - or at least hear!- Pandemonium! Something awful had happened. Unmistakeable!"

3) " Must say the Motorbike had not been backward overtaking us!"

4) " We three had sort of stuck together - because going that way does cut off a mile and a bit. He shouldn't have strayed over...."

5) " It was horrible! Could have been me! Nobody stood a chance!"

6) " From what I could see, there was no real reason for a Yamaha to be our side of the road - unless he was wanting to shorten the bend? Equally, the yellow car struck had no time at all to brake."

COLLISION TWENTY :

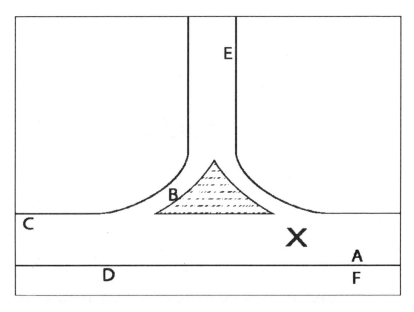

1) " I'd left the Castle's grounds a little bit earlier, then headed back . What I could see was 1 car hit at front and back at same time"

2) " I'd parked in overflow. That's why I saw it all unfolding...."

3) " Coming out of the Castle towards the main road, I could see three cars askew, and people wandering round in a mass."

4) " Could have been me! I'd been a bit delayed. 3 vehicles involved, all oddly placed: posh woman something to do with Hall."

5) " I was out of it really: concentrating on going West, not East. But I do think brown Heritage signs get covered by trees."

6) " I couldn't believe it! I wanted to rush over to calm her down! No way was she leaving enough time to use the Main Entrance!"

COLLISION TWENTY-ONE :

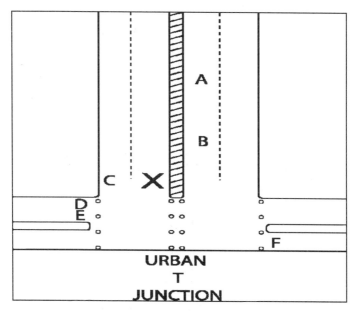

URBAN
T
JUNCTION

1) " I was surprised to see the car in front of me hitting an old man's car - which shouldn't have been emerging there anyway."

2) " I was baffled the black car attempted a Right turn on Amber- and Amber might have changed to Red already..."

3) " I was going quite fast to try to creep through on green. I wasn't really concentrating on a car near me in the wrong lane *and* carriageway!"

4) " I suppose I was nearest the collision. The old man must have been muddled! Very muddled to be going the wrong way!"

5) " The chance was no collision if nothing else wanted *that* lane."

6) " I was due to go Left into the slower lane, not as black car did."

31

COLLISION TWENTY-TWO :

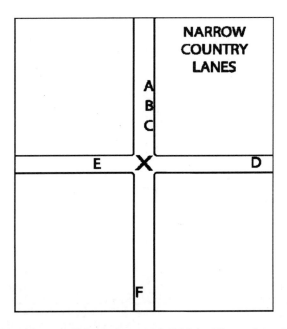

1) "Although I was doing some speed, I think - I hope- I would have been more aware of that crossing."

2) " In the distance I could see fast approaching lights, then bang!"

3) " I hate these lanes : giving way, and I wondered how the quick car ahead of me would manage the crossroad? Now I know!"

4) " We were bunching behind a fairly cautious driver - but from the commotion at the crossroads, one driver wasn't so careful...."

5) " My first fear was selfish : would I get squashed in the braking behind me , the braking in front?"

6) " I had a direct view : the impact was worse for the speeds...."

COLLISION TWENTY-THREE :

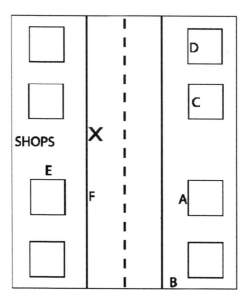

1) " It happens so often. I was about to leave the fruit shop - and noticed the Ice-Cream van on the other side of the road. Then the screams! The little girl must have been so excited after school."

2) " Between shops, I saw van, then young child + ice , running."

3) " I was still some way off, and on the other side of the road - which actually gave me a better view of the build-up overtaking."

4) " Busy road, bad light : I'd already decided to halt a while..."

5) " About to enter the shop, I had seen 3 children queueing..."

6) " Looking out my shop window, I could see this car totally committed to passing the van almost opposite, and a bit fast..."

COLLISION TWENTY-FOUR :

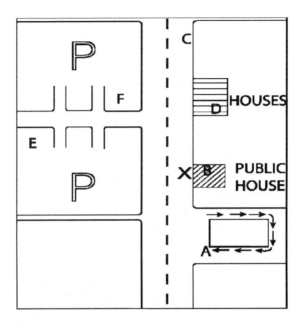

1) " I didn't get the clearest view, but I do know from the open passenger door that he'd stopped in rain to pick someone up."

2) " It was raining heavily. I don't think the courier ahead of me ever expected a suddenly parked car. Nor would I!"

3) " As I looked out my side window, I saw a lady run from the Pub to get her lift in the dry. Ironically, a delivery-man was unprepared!"

4) " I was wet! And a lot of cars parked up - but some crash!"

5) " I was also about to go home. She wanted to skip the puddles!"

6) " By chance, I fetched my car at the very moment UREPAK struck this punter's drop off. And The Fox has its own Car Park!"

34

COLLISION TWENTY-FIVE :

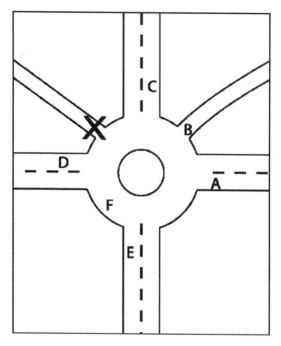

1) " I only saw the unseated motorcyclist passing. He seemed very sensible, so would have assumed his chosen exit was clear."

2) " I suppose I'm Witness One. The motorbike had no way of knowing there would be two vehicles side-by-side when he left..."

3) " I was going slow: to turn Left, maybe without having to stop."

4) " I was about to enter the Roundabout when I glanced Right and saw how a stalled or telephoning car effectively caused a blockage."

5) " I could not believe it : a committed bike suddenly cut off..."

6) " The collision happened a few seconds before I saw the danger."

COLLISION TWENTY-SIX :

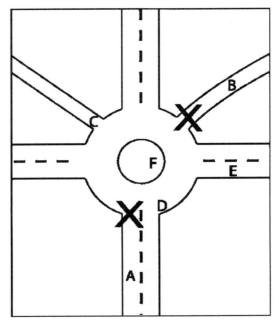

1) " It was so snowy : vehicles were skidding Left & Right..."

2) " I had to do the Roundabout in 2nd.Gear : immediately ahead of me a people-carrier swerving into an emerging car - without notice."

3) " No way could the two cars that passed me stop in time!"

4) " I could hear vehicles smashing into each other , going far too fast for the conditions. Still difficult to attribute blame it seems?"

5 " The snow was heavy and wet; it could have been me entering!"

6) " It was so bad underfoot that I thought it safest in the middle - which gave me views I didn't expect : 2 crashes, not one."

COLLISION TWENTY-SEVEN :

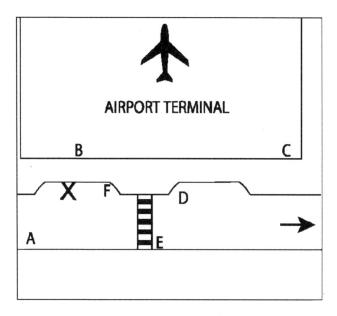

1) " I was just coming out of Terminal One when I spotted a car all surrounded by bent trolleys. The baggage handler looked amazed!"

2) " Like the rest I could only stop for 10 minutes max. Preparing to leave, another car about to leave misjudged the trolley-man."

3) " I'd just been dumped and then this almighty clash behind me!"

4) " I wasn't quite ready to go back - so I looked out of this huge window and saw this snake of trolleys severed in two!"

5) " On my Left, this disgraced - & fined - driver taking his rage out on all these harmless trolleys. *They really mean 10 minutes only*!"

6) " I needed to cross. Too much going on all over the compound!"

COLLISION TWENTY-EIGHT :

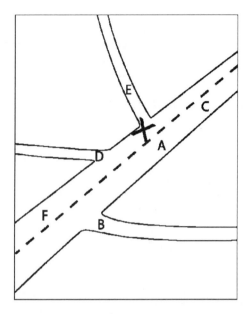

1) " Great big Prom Limousine! Pink! Couldn't miss it! Or could you? I was about to meet her - and she was, in fairness, signalling."

2) " I don't think the driver was concentrating. Music far too loud! I could hear it right next to me : thump! thump! And laughter..."

3) " Although I was some way behind, the cyclist was acting impeccably. She could not have known what the Limo might do."

4) " I was about to turn Left and the Limousine was set straight on."

5) " It was awful! I think this Limo only signalled at last minute..."

6) " My eyes were set down the road, not up - but I still heard this piercing scream - a woman's scream - from behind the joy-riders."

COLLISION TWENTY-NINE :

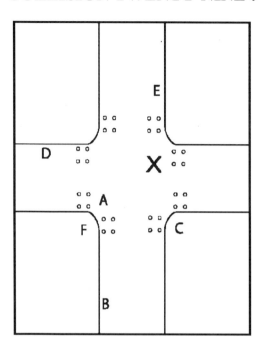

1) " I wasn't the first in line to enter this junction - but I did have time to see one little old lady turn Right without looking...."

2) " As I waited for the Green Man, I saw one driver go through very slowly, then quicken up to turn Right - which she couldn't."

3) " I knew I'd never get through on green - but one Nissan had - and seemed to think the forward lane has automatic priority..."

4) " As I waited to cross, I saw this elderly driver map-reading!"

5) " As a cyclist, I could squeeze through. She misjudged it...."

6) " The car ahead of me braked really suddenly -but to no avail."

COLLISION THIRTY :

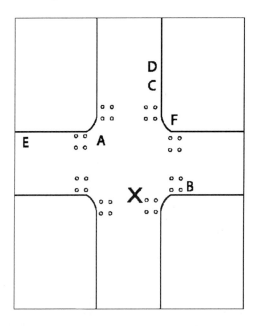

1) " I think the U-turning Taxi completely forgot *my* approach!"

2) "Waiting, I didn't see much - but knew the U-turn was fatal."

3) " I was going to cross by foot - so I saw it all. That Taxi's U-turn *might* have worked, until he ran out of time, ran out of room."

4) " The lights are quite long on Red - but the empty flat-back lorry was travelling slower than how the Taxi judged it. Very risky!"

5) " I knew I'd be on Red - but the Taxi had time to spare, if only!"

6) " I braked to give the Taxi chance to turn - but the odds were clearly against such a manoeuvre - complicated by a late arrival."

COLLISION THIRTY-ONE :

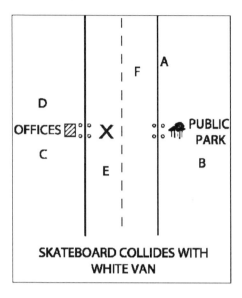

SKATEBOARD COLLIDES WITH WHITE VAN

1) "I'd been in the Park and was leaving. I think the skateboarder half thought he'd wait - then thought he'd enough time to go..."

2) " I think I was heading for the same crossing. The white van involved was going pretty smart-ish for the uphill..."

3) " The skateboard would soon have been in front of *me !*"

4) " Looking out of the top window, the Red Man had lit up...A few seconds earlier, it might have been flashing Green Man...."

5) " From my top window, I thought how rusty & shabby the van."

6) " Yes, I had been passed by that van - and on a hill. My heart sank when I saw the Skateboarder going ahead on our Green..."

COLLISION THIRTY-TWO :

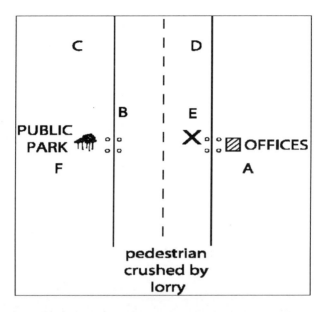

pedestrian
crushed by
lorry

1) " I could see this Jogger running really fast out of the Park. I can only imagine that, under headphones, she thought she could do it..."

2) " I was still in the park when the rain started. The jogger had passed me at steady speed - and ahead showed no slowing down..."

3) " I wish I'd never parked up! I knew the lorry wouldn't stop!"

4) " I was as wrong by tailgating the HGV. He had to proceed come what may, thinking in his head no pedestrian would tempt fate..."

5) " I heard the terrible screams. Yes traffic was quite unrelenting."

6) " By then the Jogger had successfully dodged me, only to think - I suppose she did think - any oncoming traffic would slow up."

42

COLLISION THIRTY-THREE

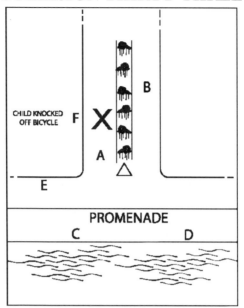

1) " When I saw 5 excitable young women getting out of this titchy Fiat, and the sprawled out pedal-bike, I imagined the very worst!"

2) " There are quite a few trees in the centre of this Seaside approach road. But I reckon I heard the child wailing *beforehand*!"

3) " I knew from all the panic a child was injured. Holidaymakers!"

4) " I ran to help the poor little girl with cuts and bruises. I didn't really have time to rescue her precious bike before *it* was run over."

5) " First I knew of it was the Ambulance. Then I said: 'Oh God!'"

6) " I didn't see the actual impact. I hate it when poor bikers suffer - especially children. So avoidable! Why mix different road-users?

COLLISION THIRTY-FOUR :

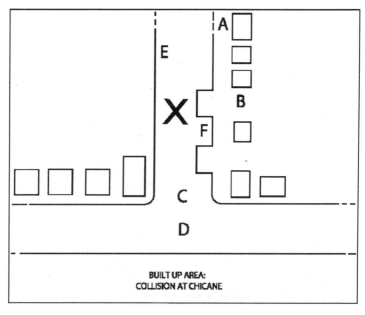

BUILT UP AREA:
COLLISION AT CHICANE

1) " I was just waiting to leave the side road, having just been passed, and nearly hit by what looked like a 15-year old tearaway."

2) " I was getting in the bin and saw neither car giving way...."

3) " As I came out of the house 2 cars crashed, an old 1 at speed!"

4) " I was taking a short cut. These chicanes, also trees, were put in to discourage through traffic here. This kid must be an outsider."

5) " How did the teens who overtook me fare ? Now I know!"

6) " When I heard the screeching of brakes behind me, I instinctively jumped. A parked car just setting out was not so lucky. These two old dears are shaken, but uninjured. Some nightmare!"

COLLISION THIRTY-FIVE :

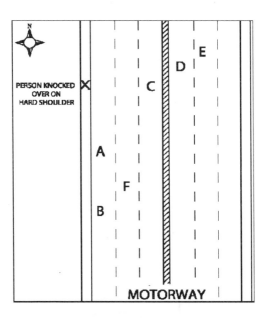

1) " If I could see the yellow flashing light of Breakdown, I'm sure this silver car could have done the same. Was he asleep ?"

2) " Breakdowns do happen, but this silver car had been meandering - phoning? - and looking unsure about lane discipline."

3) " Straining to see the far carriageway, I noted this silver saloon not appear to slow down at all for Emergency..."

4) " Yes I was nearest. The breakdown man had no earthly chance!"

5) " I knew there'd be trouble when a silver car a little ahead seemed to straddle slow lane and hard shoulder."

6) " Though I was going fast, I could yet pick out an upraised bonnet and the inevitability of it all : an open and shut case!"

COLLISION THIRTY-SIX :

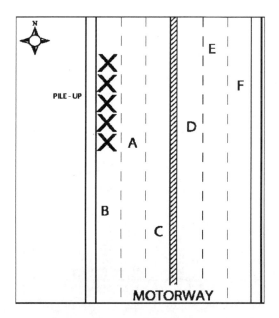

1) " Difficult to know smoke from fog. I was committed to the fast lane and became a potential rubber-necker : seeing it all unfold."

2) " Wish I hadn't been in a fast lane with all that fog - but at least I was relatively safe without a lead-driver suddenly slowing...."

3) " I'd already slowed right down, to give me more control...."

4) " How glad I was to be far enough back to hear all the crashes, determined to warn drivers behind of all the hazard to come."

5) " Daft I was really to be trying to keep to 60 in all the swirl...."

6) " All the time I was seeing cocoa tins, I was dreading ricochet."

COLLISION THIRTY-SEVEN :

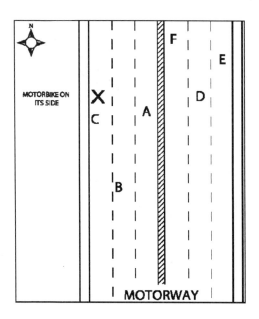

1) " I wasn't really concentrating on that carriageway, but I do know that motorbike travelled ages and ages on its side: awful!"

2) " This poor bike came in front of me from nowhere : still on its side. I had initially seen it further ahead - before its skidding...."

3) " I'd guess this bike was thrown askew by sudden lane changes"

4) " Whoever brushed against whom, the white driver sped away! That white car somehow touched the bike or unsettled it"

5) " Going so slow, I did catch sight of a rider propelled all over..."

6) " Suddenly the Yamaha that had been passing me was in trouble, dreadful trouble. Was it loss of control, or was he struck somehow?"

COLLISION THIRTY-EIGHT :

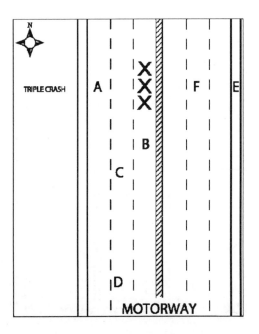

1) " Thank Goodness I was in the inner lane! I've never seen torrential rain like it. We all almost stopped on the shoulder.."

2) " I could foresee bunching in the fast lane : the spray!"

3) " Just as I proceeded South, under a cloud-burst, I just spotted cars going into each other on the opposite carriageway..."

4) " I kept contemplating going at 20 or 30 till the rains abated. Poor so-and-so's in the fast lane couldn't see when to draw in!"

5) " I did something illegal - but then I became the best Witness!"

6) " Stupid I was, stuck out there! At least I'd left 30yards or so - but what's 30 yards at 70 miles? I cursed myself for not slowing."

COLLISION THIRTY-NINE :

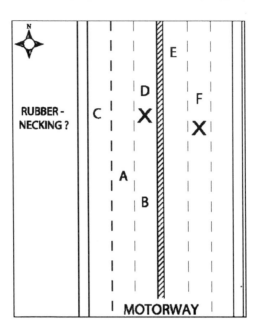

1) " Not far ahead of me : tailgating too bad even for lorries! One crunch, then another! Perhaps another one soon?"

2) " In my rear view mirror I could see my followers colliding...."

3) " Hard to see who was first! I told myself : CONCENTRATE!"

4) " How I survived, I know not! I was just braking because those in front of me were in trouble - when the other side were crashing."

5) " I came away safest because I let, left, whatever was : be...."

6) " Multiple distractions. Fancy two brightly-coloured lorries - household names - colliding! I could just imagine the fool who'd overtaken me wanting to see what was up!"

COLLISION FORTY :

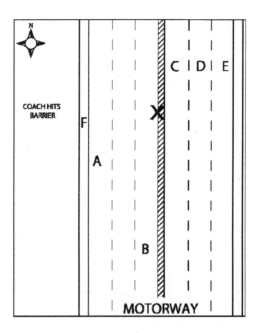

1) " Heavy build-up of traffic: so I couldn't shift lane, even to help that poor coach swerving towards the barrier - and me!"

2) " No way could a coach go at that speed with noisy kids on it!"

3) " By chance, my radiator overheating, I saw the coach go into the central barrier so powerfully that it might have flipped over!"

4) " Straight ahead of me, the Bus was really struggling: big time!"

5) " Luckily we'd all slowed, so I was near at hand for Emergency."

6) " Technically I was nearest: thus likeliest to be crushed if this coach had jumped, as high shoe-box coaches *do* jump..."

50

COLLISION FORTY-ONE :

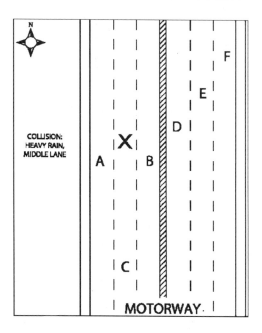

1) " It was all so far away - but because I was going fairly slow, I could work out a bit of what was happening : quite a big shunt...."

2) " Traffic was specially heavy all over. I'd signalled for Left but couldn't - and sports-car involved seemed to be flashing full beam!"

3) " I had time to see the actual crunch. Back car couldn't wait!"

4) " I was far too committed but did see a front car panicking..."

5) " Traffic build-ups always a problem. In all the spray, I was foolishly bound to stay in the middle of 2 lines - like him!"

6) " Unwittingly, I might have *caused* all this : by staying on 70 exactly, and encouraging this geezer to weave past me on inside..."

COLLISION FORTY-TWO :

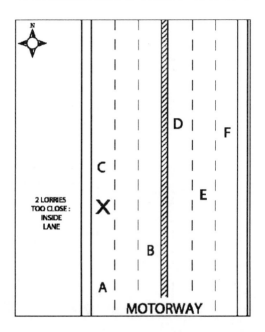

1) "I'm an HGV driver too! It's chaos when everyone bunches! The whole collision was inevitable the moment the French lorry *raced*."

2) " As a truck driver, I dread Monday mornings. Too little space!"

3) " Funnily, my lane was quiet. Opposite, freight was signalling..."

4) " There was no point taking my wagon into the middle, because none of us could mount that hill! One *foreign* lorry kept edging out."

5) " It was all happening to the Left of me : jockeying for position."

6) " As I drew parallel, I couldn't help noticing nobody giving way. Whether one trucker revved up to bully another, we'll never know. The trouble is : there's only so much road, and too many loads."

COLLISION FORTY-THREE :

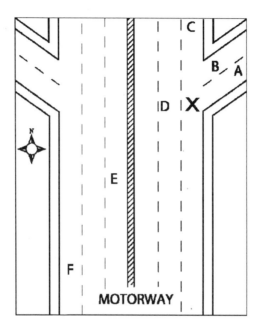

1) " I'm convinced the SUV in front of me was accelerating : to try
in vain to beat anyone and everyone already on the Motorway..."

2) " Pity the poor blighter next to me, minding his own business..."

3) " A long way across, I could see lots of traffic coming South -
and merging wasn't working. Merging's *an art* : COMPROMISE!"

4) " As soon as there was a pusher, that pusher was bound to get
unstuck! I saw it all unfold - and braked heavily..."

5) " I got perhaps the clearest view. No way was there any gap!"

6) " Could have been me! Luckily I read the road better - knowing
I might have to come to a complete halt if nobody would give way."

COLLISION FORTY-FOUR :

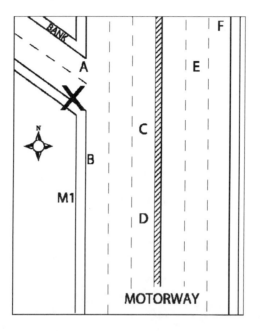

1) " Something made me look to my Right. I could just see bales of hay falling off a departing wagon. Very tight for others leaving M1"

2) " I wasn't leaving but could see this straw tumbling all over..."

3) " As I signalled Left/ Left, I saw one of the cars ahead of me showered , dented, beneath these very weighty bundles of hay."

4) " I always had doubts about *the stability* of flat-back lorries piled so high with Winter feed. How this one wobbled! centre of gravity!"

5) " Alongside a stricken vehicle -2!- I managed to dodge danger."

6) " I spotted the lorry driver struggling to keep his high load on board. Maybe in the circumstances, the next car should hold back"

COLLISION FORTY-FIVE :

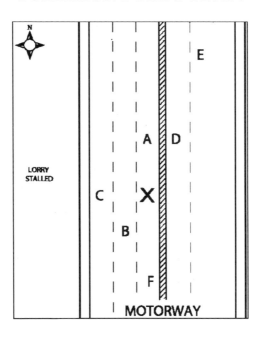

1) " I'm very lucky. When the truck stalled in the middle lane, I had time to get out of jail. Nothing passing! Did he run out of fuel?"

2) " Flashing by, I saw *2* cars shattered : classic side / side impact!"

3) " What do you do if there's a stall in the middle lane? Nothing except brake hard with your hazards on. Overtaking is a peril!

4) " Lucky or unlucky? I was on the safe side of the crash. I could get by with ease. This other crew must have failed the mirrors' test."

5) " I was still a fraction behind. Someone was already *in* this lane."

6) " I got some view, despite needing to keep myself on course. No way was the car immediately behind the lorry free. Wrong call!"

COLLISION FORTY-SIX :

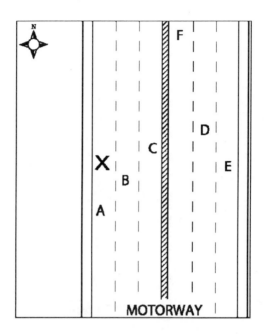

1) " I had time to see the crash - though across many lanes. I noticed a blue Fiesta with hazards on for ages, then slowing..."

2) " I had hardly any time to see the collision - but I didn't see the car in trouble try to reach the shoulder. Was he sending a Text?"

3) " Just behind, I was surprised Mum & kids ever *stayed* behind..."

4) " All the action was behind me! The little I saw of the stricken blue car, he was everso erratic, uncertain? Was he on the phone?"

5) " In a flash I saw a full car pile into the back of the empty..."

6) " I saw everything. The poor woman driver taking this chancer at value may have stayed behind him for an Exit soon to come up?"

COLLISION FORTY-SEVEN :

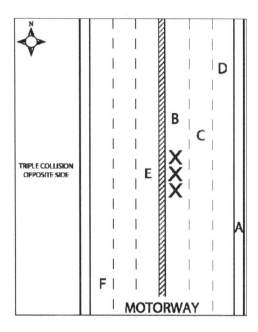

1) " Hell's Bells! I was right alongside! Carnage and chaos!"

2) " Funny! I'd stopped to report spilt oil to the Police. I was certain I myself had skidded on spilt oil. But nobody could warn the rest!"

3) " Right behind, losing traction, I somehow shuddered to a halt!"

4) " I had time to see some of the lead-up. Miracle: only 3 crashed!"

5) " For up to a mile, cars were struggling. Then, a little way ahead, the inevitable tragedy. Cars began sliding on *a worse* patch of oil."

6) " I was lucky because I'd been travelling along where nowt was dumped on the road. But those three- 4? - suffered *terrible* skids. And, even though they didn't slow down, they were kyboshed!"

57

COLLISION FIFTY :

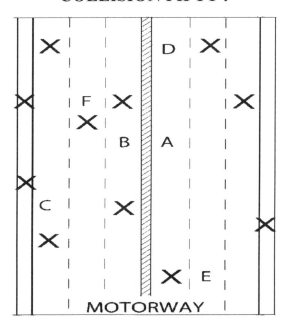

1) " They say you can do nothing in freezing rain. Second gear helped me, but not the car passing me which slid into another."

2) " On that uphill stretch, I got myself boxed in on three sides!"

3) " I think I survived in Lane 3 because of my special radial anti-skid tyres. The ice had only just started & copped 2 on my inside."

4) " I wish I'd listened! Instead 4 crashes on all 4 sides of me!"

5) " Other cars allowed me to stay on course till I could stop..."

6) " If you've got to be anywhere in freezing rain, be in the slow lane, like me. Even so, I saw more crashes that dull, drizzly, morning than in all my life up till then. Nobody could handle it!"

COLLISION FIFTY-ONE :

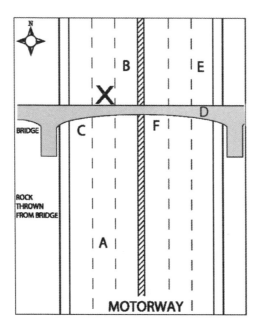

1) " I just got the idea the lads were up to no good. I was slow, so able to see the rock land, right through the screen. Did it kill him?"

2) " There's this footbridge with people on it. Then ahead, the hit!"

3) " I just saw something in my rear mirror - and boys running...."

4) " These ne'er-do-wells! I ran as if to catch the culprit -who fled."

5) " It could - or should - have been me, but I got under, unscathed. I think if I'd have changed lane, this lad would have earmarked me."

6) " These bridges rarely bother me. Somehow I was not the selected victim. Good job the boy - the killer! -was a few feet across, so that rock took the quickest route :still deadly accurate!"

COLLISION FIFTY-TWO :

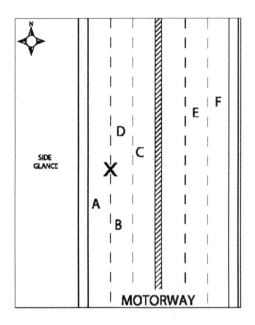

1) " Quite a lot of trucks on the road. That car transporter was huge - and carried about a dozen! Wouldn't argue with him!"

2) " I was just behind the transporter when he went in too soon. I imagine the purple car couldn't prepare- not in the Slow Lane.."

3) " I'd met this big guy a few minutes earlier. Seemed unaware of which lane to be in, even then! In my outside mirror, he swung in.."

4) " I wasn't too well-placed, but he was veering in smart-ish!"

5) " I'm quite shook up. This mammoth wasn't counting. No way!"

6) " I was conscious of the build-up. There was simply too many vehicles on his inside for him to switch - including the purple Mini."

62

COLLISION FIFTY-THREE :

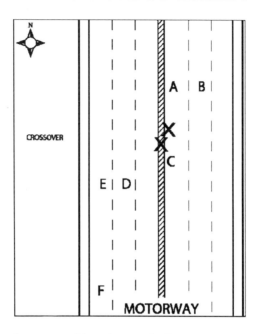

1) " I was just approaching the coned off area in the dark. And then this Luton van crossed over, straight into the gold SUV..."

2) " I'm the luckiest woman alive! Just a few seconds too early!"

3) " One lane coned off. And a 50 limit. Then in slow motion a little box van ploughs into the opposite carriageway. Was he asleep??"

4) " I wasn't easily able to help as on a Sunday evening, not late, this restricted lane was very, very, full. The cute van never braked!"

5) " I was some way back. Couldn't see any reason for the tragedy."

6) " I saw it happening!. When the van reached the temporary concrete block, it jumped it and struck the 4 x 4 really hard on."

COLLISION FIFTY-FOUR :

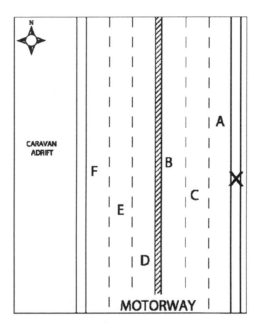

1) " I had my pedal right down - but still saw this stray caravan..."

2) " As I got almost parallel, this lone caravan finally reached a barrier tougher than itself! In seconds, it split apart! Matchwood!"

3) " I braked hard, wherever this caravan was going. Then crunch!"

4) " I'm really shaken - and guilty! It is *my* caravan that went adrift! When it first started to sway, it hijacked *us*! Now out of its misery!"

5) " I saw most of the action in slow-motion: caravan steering car!"

6) " I think the caravan's owner should be given a medal! That skilled driver refused, simply refused, to be thrown off balance, thrown off course, by his delinquent van! They're not well built!"

COLLISION FIFTY-FIVE :

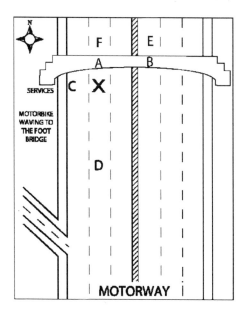

1) " I love looking down on the road! Now this guy was waving so enthusiastically, you'd think he was Beckham! But it unseated him."

2) " Gosh! He was waving *at me*! If only I'd ignored him! No fun!"

3) " Unluckily, I was right behind him, then beside him! How he waved so happily 1 moment, then went clean on his side the next."

4) " I just couldn't make it out. Why would anybody at 65 miles an hour gaze upwards, let alone *wave*? Showmen aren't fun if dead!"

5) " I actually saw this poor bloke's head-over-heels, arse over elbow, at eye level - like a very bad dream! Hope he survives...."

6) " I'd already passed this hero a bit back. *A proper Easy Rider*!"

COLLISION FIFTY-SIX :

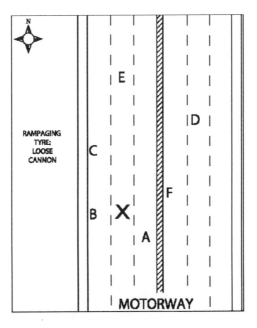

1) " I was running *beside* this runaway tyre. And the only way this saga was going to end was by the tyre mounting a bonnet- as it did!"

2) " I'd like to catch *the owner* of this huge tyre -which passed me."

3) " I never thought a tyre took on a life of its own. Knowing I was safe, I could slow down to see how it went : causing awful havoc!"

4) " First dread : would it crush *me*? Talk about *Apocalypse Now*!"

5) " At the last minute it close the dinky *Ka* right next to me! She and her littl'uns didn't stand a chance! It finds you out, the Reaper!"

6) " Conditions were good. And I was zooming along. But soon I saw this bouncing 4-foot high tyre! Aiming for me? Or *under* me?"

COLLISION FIFTY-SEVEN :

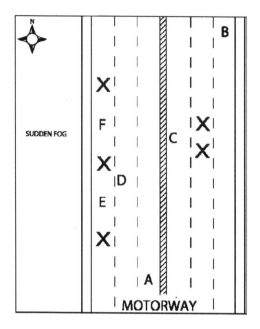

1) " My car has very good fog lamps. Fortunately, I decided to stay exactly where I was, but doing more 50 than 70. Lots of collisions!"

2) " I think it was High Pressure fog. So I chose to dawdle at 25..."

3) " Crash ahead, crash behind! I needed the safety of drawing in!"

4) " There is a big difference between stopping, and going, in fog. You get all disorientated when there is no vision. My main concern when fools went into each other - then others! - was our *safety*!"

5) " By staying in *that* lane, I miraculously avoided the worst...."

6) " Like a zombie, I went too fast, past all these shunts shunting."

COLLISION FIFTY-EIGHT :

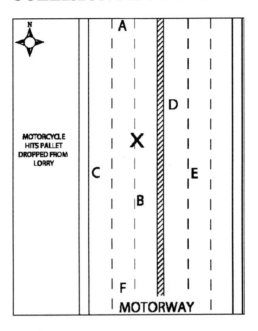

1) " I did see the pallet being dropped off the back of a builder's lorry - which definitely didn't stop. Settled in the biker's path!"

2) " My first knowledge was seeing a bike tumbling ahead..."

3) " In a second, this wide motorcycle struck a platform of wood. If the biker *was* a man, he could not have avoided it. Criminal!"

4) " I only saw the skidding pallet. I remember thinking : *Disaster!*"

5) " I was straight behind the unlucky bike. Could have been me! Sad it caught *him* - though his machine was, unusually, 3-wheeled!"

6) "From the *outside* lane, I was livid at carelessly shed detritus..."

COLLISION FIFTY-NINE :

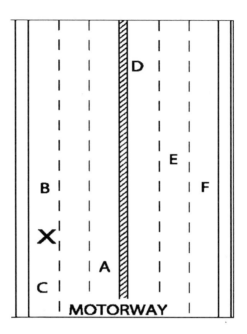

1) " I was coming up parallel with the bread-van that suddenly shot into the truck ahead of him. He must have been suddenly taken ill..."

2) " I was the first HGV in a queue. Behind me: he drove OK!"

3) " My milk tanker was just behind the van that lurched - almost thrust itself - into the French wagon ahead of it. It made no sense!"

4) " I'm used to trucks bunching -but this looked different, strange."

5) " I was getting nearer that group of lorries all the time. The weather and light were splendid. I'm baffled how it happened..."

6) " Only the metallic clash - unmistakeable! - alerted me to what was happening. *Then* the tragedy entered my consciousness."

COLLISION SIXTY :

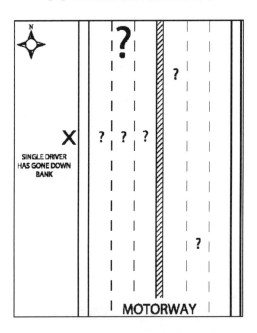

EARLY ONE SUNDAY MORNING, TWO VEHICLES, EACH WITH FALSE NUMBER PLATES (?), WERE RACING SO DETERMINEDLY, SIDE-BY-SIDE, THAT THE INSIDE CAR JUMPED THE SIDE CRASH-BARRIER AND CAREERED DOWN THE BANK TOWARDS A BROOK. EVEN AT 2am., THERE WERE PROBABLY 5 *ADDITIONAL* WITNESSES. WHAT WERE THEIR *SIX* EXCUSES FOR NOT STOPPING AT THE SCENE? :

1)

2)

3)

4)

5)

6)

COLLISION SIXTY [EXTRA] :

What are *these* witnesses describing ? :

" This is a major trunk road....the Highways' Agency were just saving money...."

" We always said this would happen!"

" Pity the little Fiat. It didn't have a chance."

" Thank Goodness we were a couple of minutes late checking whether we'd locked the front door!"

" I could sense the black S.U.V. wasn't really holding the road. It certainly had a lot of people in it."

" I think the Mum was distracted by something, maybe a tape - or some of the kids arguing."

" The children trying to escape couldn't go anywhere without being run over by fast cars passing."

" A few of the over-takers didn't even stop!"

" We waited, hoping, the old dears in the Fiat would get out. No such luck!"

" The speed on this 3-mile by-pass is often faster than the M1 itself."

" Wonder why she pulled out? She'd only just joined us!"

===?

fault : ==?

COLLISION SIXTY-ONE :

What are *these* witnesses describing ? :

" I think he was seventy."

" Always there, rain or shine!"

" Good way with children....seemed to have time for them. Each day you could see him chatting and joking."

" I think he was fearless. All us regulars respected him!"

" A lot of the children and their Mums were hysterical."

" The two hoodies seemed to run away. Pity the poor yob left in the back seat!"

" He looked a bit dazed but I think he was wearing a seat-belt. That certainly stopped him flying."

" Three or four cars parked half on the pavement might have cluttered up the road at that particular point."

" Old-fashioned isn't it ? Like we might have done it in the 1950s."

" Good job one of the teachers had nursing training. She was doing CPR like billio !"

" Police car seemed to arrive mighty quick! Maybe only three vehicles behind....."

" I'd describe it as a dank November morning, cold, definitely no frost or black ice."

" The minibus coming towards us - and him - seemed to be going slow, and was right prepared - sort of."

==?

fault : ================================?

COLLISION SIXTY-TWO :

What are *these* witnesses describing ?

" Difficult to understand why they do it."

" You see them every day! I supposed they can't be bothered!"

" It's as if one does it, then the rest copy!"

" They put it up in the 1980s. New housing and all that!"

" I think 3-30's a bad time. Particularly when the clocks have gone back."

" Although it's a 40 area, I guess most people see the way the road goes and think it's 60."

" There was always going to be one casualty. I couldn't ever picture more than one!"

" Maybe all three misjudged the speed."

" To see the rucksacks! Awful."

" Just happened to be drawing the curtains at that very moment. Stupid! I could leave them another hour but don't."

" I'd gone right down to about 28.....could sense danger.."

" Difficult to say if this delivery fan could have stopped sooner. Yes the driver did get out okay, shocked."

" Could have been me I s'pose. Don't know what more the County Council could have done."

" About 10 cars suddenly screeched to a halt."

======================================= ?

fault : ==============================?

73

COLLISION SIXTY-THREE :

What are *these* witnesses describing ?

" A lot of them are bored stiff. It's so straight!"
" A lot of them are working to a deadline. Maybe they've just promised to meet someone in the pub at 9 o'clock. Daft really."
" Difficult to see really. Certainly something dreadfully wrong....but far too far ahead to see the build-up."
" Only one man I think. Very well-dressed. Suit and tie-only ; he'd taken off his jacket, and it was freezing!"
" Easy to get sleepy if you've woken that early!"
" Rusty old tractor! Not good for owt else!"
" They shouldn't allow them to do it! And I hear they're going to have more of them!"
" Quite a lot to read. Quite a complicated message. And quite a bit of money off!"
" I don't think they can do much about it with it being private land."
" How that motorcycle did not follow, I'll never know? Must have nerves of steel!"
" Front job. Will definitely have to be towed away!"

==?

fault : ==============================?

COLLISION SIXTY-FOUR :

What are *these* witnesses describing ?

" Yes, it was in a mighty hurry."

" Brand new! State of the art! Lots of ladders!"

" I think all these men in helmets - and they were all men- would rather have been somewhere else...where they were meant to be! I suppose none of us like to be held up."

" From what I saw in my rear mirror, although he was weaving, he was visible enough to know he was on his way."

" Well I've learnt something new today! I always thought Red was Red, Green, Green - until they changed."

" I think that hatchback did have right-of-way. Yes she did have right-of-way. I'm pretty sure she wasn't jumping lights like the other fella!"

" Might is right!"   " Needs must!"

" I'm lucky really, I was just waiting my Right as I always do, every day. You certainly don't expect to get through the very first time."

" Must have been an awkward place before it was re-modelled."

" It's all coming back to me now! I was actually facing!"

======================================?

fault : ==============================?

COLLISION SIXTY-FIVE :

What are *these* witnesses describing ?

" I don't think Jim and Maeve were anywhere else 'cept where they normally are....."

" Jim is part of a scheme to get early-warning. Don't think he got early warning this time!"

" It's complicated having the lavvies out there too."

" Bodies everywhere! Laid out everywhere!"

" Nearly all lads...but two high-heeled girls were screaming!"

" We have had a bit of gangland these past two years."

" And I was only walking the dog! It's not normally like this!"

" When I looked out of the bedroom window, it seemed it confirmed everything we've always said!"

" Will be difficult for Police to know whether it's private or public land. Police hardly ever come this way!"

" A lot of the lads had split lips, broken noses."

" By the time Ambulance turned up, I think they's freed this particular lad. He might pull through. Doubt it!"

" I suppose he and missus were just going home..."

" In the darkness, only had a few seconds. Both really!"

===================================?

fault : ===============================?

COLLISION SIXTY-SIX :

What are these witnesses describing ?

" We were all looking up! You have to, don't you?

" I couldn't understand holding it Midsummer?"

" This road is busy any day - and on Saturday going to the seaside!"

" They're remarkable operators!"

" Thousands turn up. Real nutters! Year after year!"

" So when you're looking up, you're not really looking where you're going."

" The lights were ahead! Quite a cross-road!"

" Gorgeous weather! I think we all had our windows down!"

" There's no judging what all these people will do in the holidays ; lots of kids too!"

" Think the queues had disappeared 3 hours earlier. Was quite quiet really. Certainly free-flowing."

" You don't normally see such a big vehicle at the Weekend...not as long as that."

" Somehow these 2 ladies got out. Both about 50."

" The Angels were awake today! Nobody at all at the back!"

" Could have been worse. Lesson to us all."

======================================?

fault : ==============================?

77

COLLISION SIXTY-SEVEN :

What are these witnesses describing ?

" Suicide. definitely!"

" Notorious spot really! Always has been!"

" Both of them! What a waste!"

" All their lives ahead of them!"

" At least it happened for both at the same time...like in each other's arms."

" The skid-marks tell it all. Very deep! Very, very deep!"

" I wonder if he braked at the last minute? We'll never know - will we?"

" Cloudy afternoon , but none of that low-hanging fog."

" Quiet road, really. Very quiet!"

" From what I could see, no other vehicle involved."

" The car right behind was tail-gating. No excuse for that. In far too much hurry in my reckoning."

" I think I got the last view of the driver. Was with the grandkid. Afternoon out. Look of wild determination on the man's face."

" Wonder whether she tried to get out, or was resigned?"

" Open and shut for the investigators, I reckon..."

===?

fault :   ===============================?

COLLISION SIXTY-EIGHT :

What are these witnesses describing ?

" I was clearly beckoning him. People should have been watching my arms."

" Daddy was only trying to get Mummy's car ready for tomorrow morning...."

" I must say I was a bit confused at first as he seemed to be driving towards me."

" It was quite a big house fronting on to the road, with a double-width drive : definitely one that could take 2 cars."

" Yes I was cleaning the inside window 2 doors down from where it all happened. It was like in slow motion."

" Although it was 5-ish in the afternoon, I think there was enough light to work out what he was aiming for."

" I'd overtaken him a second or two earlier. Nothing about such a slow-coach that I'd not have expected on a country 'B' road."

"He'd probably done something similar with Car Number One before he tackled Car number two."

" The car which came off worse was not speeding, definitely not speeding - but not a local either."

" Those shooting-brakes tend to stand a bit higher...."

==?

fault : ===============================?

79

COLLSION SIXTY-NINE :

What are these witnesses describing ?

" I've heard of drug barons going in for that sort of thing - but not motorbikes."

" You expect these big powerful machines to weave in and out...but not at the wrong times!"

" Wonder whether he was born-again, rather than a rookie ?"

" I don't think the girl could have done more. Maybe she tried to."

" I just caught a glance of the agonized expression on the girl's face."

" Must have been an emergency stop. I've probably only seen one or two of those in my whole life! Gosh, how I needed to be on my toes!"

" Yes the road is laid out for 50, and I hazard he was doing about 60 : a lot!"

" That morning was quite dark. No ice but must of been low visibility."

" Poor bloke!"

" Middle of the road's a damned awkward place to be in. You're probably in everybody's blind-spot."

==?

fault : ================================?

COLLISION SEVENTY :

What are these witnesses describing ?

" She was potentially stranded in that dedicated Right Turn lane...."

" She couldn't really get out and check. You can't leave a car in the middle of the highway!"

" The 2 or 3 vehicles behind her were getting impatient...very impatient!"

" It's easy to say someone shouldn't be swayed by whoever is behind you...."

" Amazingly, some cars coming in the opposite direction didn't seem to experience the same problem."

" I think the Highway Code says edge forward cautiously -if that happens...."

" She was dead unlucky how it worked out."

" That Junction had to have them....too busy not to."

" Things are different late at night. You don't know whether there has been a problem earlier on."

" Maybe she misunderstood the sequence. Who knows? The sequence might have been CCTV monitor-controlled...or she might have been an inch or two back from the sensor."

" The other vehicle was certainly in a mighty hurry!"

=====================================?
fault : ==================================?

81

COLLISION SEVENTY-ONE :

What are these witnesses describing ?

" I think the single-decker had only just pulled out of the Bus Stop - so he decided not to split them up."

" At first it was very ordered. I counted up to 5 before everyone had had enough."

" Maybe one more came out...certainly I counted quite a few auxiliaries."

" Remarkable, really, that in 2015 people would do that!"

" Risky! Both lead vehicles have to be in total agreement!"

" Funny! At first it looked like all of them would have to stay where they were!"

" Almost non-stop flow at 9-45 in the morning!"

" Perhaps vehicle number 8 or whatever had got a bit separated 5 minutes beforehand - or had not joined the first flow speedily enough."

" Pity the poor fellow who thought he'd got the nod!"

" Shows you don't always get thanks for doing the right thing!"

" No man's land is an uncomfortable place to be!"

" Nearly got there hitching a different sort of lift!!"

===?

fault : =================================?

COLLISION SEVENTY-TWO :

What are these witnesses describing ?

" Yes there was a lane of sorts - though cars were allowed to park on it."

" I had to turn my eyes away!"

" An awful lot of screaming : hysterical screaming."

"At first it didn't look as if the white van would stop."

" I wouldn't like to vouch his indicator was on."

" On or off would have made no difference..."

" That's when one like him is on to a loser."

" Maybe a bit safer on a Sunday morning."

" I don't think he even had time to raise the alert..."

" Daft isn't it ? Putting the village name on the actual turning...when everybody's committed."

" I suppose the only alternative is to go up to the top of the hill then down again."

" Some squeeze!"

" Maybe one of his mirrors was badly adjusted..."

" Would two have made the difference? Not sure."

" Some of these modern hi-visibilities are fantastic!"

" Fifteenth one this year in the Capital!"

" Speed wasn't a factor. Not really."

" He and his mate will have to live with it for decades!"

" A waste! But I doubt if Council will take any heed..."

===?

fault : ===================================?

COLLISION SEVENTY-THREE :

What are these witnesses describing ?

" It's going to take ages and ages for the three Insurance Companies to settle this one."

" Yes it's tight. Very tight!"

" You've done your shopping and you're ready to get home...especially at dinner-time."

" It was still in her teeth, poor girl."

" She'd obviously done a good job strapping them in!"

" You should have seen this very long saloon after! All bonnet, no beef!"

" Better to have your dipped head-lamps on!"

" The Council *were* warned. Bet no Councillors go anywhere near it!"

" Difficult to know if you are better facing outwards?"

" Part of the problem is the 10-30 cut-off!"

" I don't like them! Never have!"

" I bet the first 2 Insurance will go for knock-for-knock... third Insurance a bit more tricky."

" Bet that's not what he or she wants to see after a brief sojourn in the Co-op!"

=====================================?

fault : ================================?

84

COLLISION SEVENTY-FOUR :

What are these witnesses describing ?

" I'd been counting the number of drivers on the phone. There was almost a majority!"

" I don't know what drew my attention to the tragedy?"

" The awful thing is : everybody might have been keeping the rules."

" The majority of pupils were already safely in their lessons ...it was the stragglers really...and 6th. Form."

" Two girls - friends? - screamed and screamed but I don't think he heard."

" He pulled off quite a feat stopping at the Pelican Lights in the first place : a big load to bring to a halt."

" Silly place to put a Pelican : and just before a busy Left turn, not, as would be logical, actually governing entry and exit down that minor road."

" She wasn't in uniform- but then, at 17, she wouldn't."

" Yes the lights were working : flashing amber, I recall."

" Terrible thing for anybody approaching from the opposite, school drive, side to have to see!"

" Vehicle design has got a long, long way to go....."

" Wrong time to be in the wrong place!"

" I daresay the poor girl had never thought about that..."

=================================== ?

fault : ============================?

COLLISION SEVENTY-FIVE :

What are these witnesses describing ?

" They should never be there in the first place!"

" They're all jockeying for space!"

" Some far too early...to bag a place! Some far too late... running proper late!"

" I don't envy these grandparents! Have you noticed how grandparents are getting younger?"

" Double yellows will be no help. They'll ignore anything and everything!"

" Yes, you've got some of their own bairns put at risk, never mind other people's bairns."

" One act of negligence leads to another...I think they all copy each other's bad manners!"

" I wouldn't have tried that manoeuvre!"

" I'll have a wager that nobody in her position would have had total vision : at least four directions, at least six major considerations."

" Great competition, every single day when they're there....and they're not really encouraged through the gates either."

" Maybe her husband would have pointed out the danger? Or a night watchman? Or the one behind?"

" Over and over - like a Dinky car really !"

== ?

fault : ================================== ?

COLLISION SEVENTY-SIX :

What are these witnesses describing ?

" I'm sure most mirrors aren't properly adjusted..."
" It's usually that side that's blanked out. Is it the front-seat passenger sitting there? Does that change it?"
" They've never really invented a sign to describe the awful decision - so you're living in Fool's Paradise!"
" At that speed, one missed Ministry of Transport sign- and you're bunkered!"
" I recall some widening was attempted...but not to all of this container-lorry route...on and off...no logic to it."
" Many drivers certainly feel safer in the Inside."
" When everyone's in a straight line, fast-moving, the temptation is to keep up with what you think is back of that straight line, a bit like a Formula 1 race."
"....And we've got no way of telling vehicles behind us that we *cannot* go because nobody at all will give way."
" Must be awful to see someone bombing up behind you, then not to be able to do anything about it !"
" Yet once you've been on the new layout before, you know to use a different road next time! A nightmare!"
" Complicated place to join. Elsewhere, they've sometimes separated traffic out : to *double* the entry."
" Confusing! Too little road to go round! Tell me!"

=== ?

fault : ===============================?

87

COLLISION SEVENTY-SEVEN :

What are these witnesses describing ?

" Yes, 5 o'clock on a very gloomy dusk"

" They're always wearing the wrong colour jacket..."

" How she survived, we'll never know."

" Not chicken...No! Not responding to a dare."

" And you've always got the added consideration of previously parked vehicles suddenly pulling out."

" It's when they've just popped into Spar for fags..."

" Worst place to be. You can't really go back can you?"

" And this sort of thing always happens about 50 or 100 metres from a refuge. If only!"

" Everybody, including the bus passenger were totally committed...couldn't get out of it."

" Another one would have been along in 5 minutes!"

" I don't think the driver settling up ever saw her waving....and she *was* waving to her."

" Every danger converging...."

" Yes she did put a Right indicator on. I think!"

" So you've got both vehicles overtaking , nearly opposite each other."

" Awkward place to hit each other, even at low speed."

" I wonder what the passenger's thinking now?"

=== ?

fault : ===============================?

COLLISION SEVENTY-EIGHT :

What are these witnesses describing ?

" Stones flying everywhere! Quite frightening!"

" I would have abandoned the journey : wherever that journey was heading..."

" You can't do a U-turn in those circumstances."

" The question is : was the machine tipped over by the actual impact ?"

" So where is the rider now? Didn't stay round for long!"

" Hell with all those bottles in the air too!"

" The rumour is, it wasn't milk in those milk-bottles!"

" Perhaps leaving is better than staying?"

" People like that : they're on a high. Totally unpredictable - and joined from all the side-streets."

" Let's face it ! You're in a metal capsule. Sometimes feels secure, sometimes very insecure..."

" Dreadful crunch..under those wheels!"

" An didn't all these youths cheer! They cheered and cheered when it happened."

" That meant another four running away - and everso easily identified! Hardly invisible in the crowd!"

" These days nearly always end with a torching! Part of the theatre!"

" Would have preferred a den of lions!"

=== ?

fault : ==?

COLLISION SEVENTY-NINE :

What were these witnesses describing ?

" You could see them in pairs. You could see them talking, animated like...and I don't think they wanted to be overheard..."

" Sometimes they're only going for fish-and-chips : simple as that!"

" I expected one...and then..."

" Definitely over 50 - and it is supposed to be 30..."

" You've got to think about it. Were the two drivers in cahoots?"

" Maybe it was the most sensible thing to do : stopping like that to let them all pass."

" Well it certainly helped the pair in the yellow Mini!"

" Bet that will be in flames in 3 hours time!"

" This woman came up panting, sure that when she turned round, she saw him weaving, really weaving!"

" They're not as skilled as they think they are!"

" And I think I would be a bit alarmed in the circumstances!"

" Yellow Mini was being quite sensible till that moment: nothing untoward. Of course, if you're souped up...."

" Too many macho telly programmes! Psyching ?"

=================================== ?

fault : ===============================?

COLLISION EIGHTY :

What is this witness describing ?

" I musta bin only one theer that neet. I goes t'see moon an' stars, like . In day, you meet get 4 cars N hour : them that knows it as a short-cut, like, holiday-lets, or farmer-jonnies an' thes fam'lies.

" It's reet quiet. It's co-pied by a much betta way of gettin' onta moor, t'other sida t' hill- an' not much longa walkin' like.

" So I reck'ns it was summat more okkard. He mighta bin tryin' to dump summat...unlikely cos Police'll be all ova it in mornin'; or wantid a quiet kiss and cuddl', if you sees what I means, or wuss.....

" It were chilly : very chilly. But I wasna slippin' an' slidin' on the wata on the road that froze, like. It wasna that bad. Musta bin wind. Propa cold! Blew thru' me!

"Mindya, I runs up an' tests like the bridge. Musta tak'n it unawares, right sharp it is, tight in, tight out - but not froze. Defnily not.

" Lotsa bushes 'n brambles. Lefal I call it. An' wata's deep. I couldna do nowt - tho' I's tried. Tried reet hard, I did."

====================================== ?

fault =============================== ?

COLLISION EIGHTY-ONE :

one car goes into the back of another on a suburban road at 8-25 am., Monday February 2nd:

Dorothy : " You could see her combing her hair at the wheel - and turning right round to settle the kiddie in the back seat down. Then she seemed to stop. No indicator. I think she was wanting to get something out of her handbag. Stupid woman!"

Emily : " Ordinary school day - apart from the bitter cold. The first I knew was a dreadful crunch from behind. Set me on edge all day !"

Kate : " When we heard the bang, we got straight out to see what had happened, and to assess the damage. The car behind us had her front windscreen glistening with frost: ice really. Un-cleared and skated over even by her windscreen wipers. In fairness, she had got the actual snow off her front windows, though it was at least 4 inches deep on her roof....."

Sally : " Mum's everso careful to warm up the car before we set out. And I'm sure she'd given me a kettle of hot water to clear back and front so as we could see..."

TRUTH : _____ ?

COLLISION EIGHTY-TWO :

**a Supermarket delivery van
goes into the rear nearside door of a car
just after his delivery van has turned Left:
near the Town Centre, @ Noon one Tuesday**

Paul : " I'm the stacker and runner for Home Delivery. That day we were in a bit of a hurry, as we'd had some hold-ups, and one of our customers would soon be out for the rest of the day. I was looking up an address when we struck the back door of this really angry lady. Alf's a good driver and he held his cool - simply saying her reversing was very fast."

Nancy : " I'm livid. I was gingerly coming out of my front garden, looking first Left, then Right, sure the road, a very quiet road at that time of day, was clear. Then this Grocery van came charging round the corner, straight into me. No braking. You can see that on the road..."

Alf : " As I turned by the sandwich shop, I saw there were quite a few parked cars on both sides of the road. Then this red hatchback - the lady's - suddenly shot out from the third bungalow after the sandwich shop, between two parked cars. Crucially, I noticed a planter on the front passenger seat...which isn't there now."

TRUTH : _____ ?

COLLISION EIGHTY-THREE :

On a very hot Saturday Morning in July, two cars collide in a big Municipal Car Park:

Terry : " I was waiting about 6 or 7 minutes for that slot. On a Saturday, things are always difficult. At last, on the fourth time of trying, I spotted a car packing the boot and belting up as if to get out. So I smiled at him that I wanted to go into where he was, and deliberately overshot that slot so he could get out. Then I reversed from the aisle into the lot, only to be honked, honked by this Johnny-come-lately who was swinging into exactly the same place, only forward, not backward. I had seen him in advance, but knew he would never go for it once he understood it was mine. Road rage I call it. A nasty piece of work...and look at the damage!"

Marcel : " I wish I'd got there earlier. I was going to give up and park out-of-town -when, just as I approached this choked one-way passage between two rows of Pay-&-Display vehicles, luck came to my aid. This green car front Right was all kitted up to turn Right- as he had to - to go home. So I waited till all was clear, and signalled to slide into his spot. Being Left-hand drive, I knew what I was doing. Dreadful: I'd nearly completed my swing when this other chap came at me fast.

TRUTH : _____ ?

COLLISION EIGHTY-FOUR :

On a fairly congested A-Road out of town, an aggregates' lorry takes the offside door off a parked car - and injures emerging Driver:

Lucy-Ann [from her hospital bed] : " One of the worst days of my life : this horrible, gigantic, truck bearing down on me. I was nearly out, just preparing to close the door, and edge along the side of the car to safety. Then he sped -closing the gap- looking down to his lap. So I leapt straight back into the Driver's seat...but failed in the time available. And neither I nor Cyril - back home - have heard anything from QSA."

Shaun : " I've always got half an eye open for opening doors : a terrible hazard in this job - part because I'm much higher than most of the opposition. That morning, I had good visibility. First of all I slowed down to the pace of the taxi ahead of me, trying not to tailgate or bully this woman taxi driver. One or two statics had people darting in and out. But I certainly didn't register that anybody was about to get out of the Corsa. It's not unusual these days for the Driver to stay tight whilst front passenger does the errand. I think I was leaving two or three feet from each park-er. Then, as my cab drew exactly alongside the Corsa, a bang, and screams!"

TRUTH : _____ ?

COLLISION EIGHTY-FIVE :

Two motorcycles collide head-on, on a Green Belt stretch of A-Road, opposite a Gastro-Pub

Bob : " We were going due South, no strong sunshine, just watery, and I know I had got back into normal position. Nothing more to overtake. I would say I was doing about 62 in a 60mph. limit. Then suddenly, another machine appeared straight in front of me. All I could do was hit him on the back wheel, trying to avoid his body...otherwise he'd be in the mortuary, me too!"

Grant [from his hospital bed] : " I'm very angry - as well as losing my livelihood. I've always ridden safely, only one or two minor spills on gravel or ice. I know I had a clear run ahead of me. The road was broad enough for me to overtake a slow Micra also travelling North. As I was half way through, opposite this country inn, and ready to slot back into lane, this bloke came towards me like a bat out of Hell. He seemed to come from nowhere from behind a Luton van, not looking at all. So I swerved Right to try to miss the worst impact...."

Sara : "I was Bob's pillion -luckily thrown right clear by the crash. I'm lucky. I had longer to watch the other rider. I know he was visiting that Pub, last minute like..."

TRUTH : _____ ?

COLLISION EIGHTY-SIX :

A car and a people-carrier collide at the
edge of Crescent outside Railway Station :

Sonia : " I was leaving the Railway Station after dropping off my sister. In a way, I'm glad she wasn't there- but would have been good as a witness. I wasn't in a hurry. I passed the taxi-rank okay, and came to the beginning of the public road. It was really busy. I kept looking Left and Right for the proper moment to turn Right. At last there was a bit of a gap, and the woman not wanting the Station seemed to slow down as if to help me out. I know the Right of me was fairly clear. Then this great big people-carrier which I think had been waiting behind me a minute or two dashed Right at an unorthodox angle...and I was straight into his nearside..."

Kyle : " This silly woman was leaving the Station Left, for town. She wasn't even bothering to signal Left, but her vehicle couldn't head anywhere else from where she was. So I waited patiently for her to finish; then I saw a gap both directions - so took my chance and went Right from the corner of the dotted white markings, just as you're supposed to. To my horror, and in my blind side, she had obviously changed her mind. Look at it!"

TRUTH : _____ ?

COLLISION EIGHTY-SEVEN :

A mobility scooter and a Smart Car
collide, side on, just after Pelican lights:

Jessie : " Everyone came rushing up to me - wanting to call an Ambulance. My Scooter's a complete write-off. Wicked isn't it that these young ones have no respect, just when I'd built up the confidence to go out, and to use the Post Office and Market Hall like everyone else. I'd waited as if I was a pedestrian, on the pavement, till I heard those loud beeping noises that we could all cross. Except that only one other person wanted to cross from my side. Then this little turnip of a car was screeching to a halt and knocking my Scooter - and me - clean over. They're always jumping lights, especially from that side road behind us!"

Jane : " I feel bad and sad: worried what my boyfriend and my Dad'll say about smashing straight into an invalid. And Insurance! Gosh! But I couldn't do much different. From the side road, not the main road, I was given a clear green light to turn Left - which, as lead vehicle, I did. I knew to be aware of stragglers - but this wobbly Scooter was something different. She stopped chatting with another old person and wheeled on to the road right in front of me. I still braked heavily!"

TRUTH : _____ ?

98

COLLISION EIGHTY-EIGHT :

A Pizza Delivery Van double-parks
at the far end of the Parade :

Wilf : " Leaving the main shopping street is always the same. The Council has allowed 20-minute parking, residents' only parking, and loading/and unloading. They do that to calm traffic down. When I'm just going for residential, rather than commercial, I reckon I saw OPQ Pizzas double-park on the other side of the road. I wondered why, then just carried on past the string of parked vehicles my side of the road. To my horror, as I drew level with the Pizza, this Polo came straight toward me, and we both ran out of road space. I lost my cool with the Polo geezer! I must confess I bawled at him!"

Adrian [88] " People are always saying pensioners like me shouldn't be behind the wheel - but I really didn't do nothing wrong that morning. I'd had a sight test. Brilliant! Admittedly, I was third vehicle out when this chappie ran towards somebody's front door with a pizza box. But I was only going 25-ish - and I had plenty of time. Then this other chap came straight out roadside parking two or three back, other side. And I saw no indicator...."

TRUTH : _____ ?

COLLISION EIGHTY-NINE :

**A bus kills someone waiting at the Bus-Stop
in a dedicated bay with one vehicle in already, and
it's 8pm on a drizzly March evening :**

Phil : " I feel the pits now. I'd only stopped in that lay-by - some Bus-Stops look like ordinary lay-bys - for a minute to take phone call and tell them to ring me at home in half an hour. Buses are only one an hour, so there was hardly any chance one would come straightway. Anyway, the bloke ringing me wanted more of an answer, and sod's law: the bus did come, hooting, flashing, sweeping round me so bad that he knocked over the little old lady who'd stood further out to hail him down. I was wrong - but not guilty of woman-slaughter!"

PSV 87 : " I've told the cops all this - so I've got to wait the Inquest. But this car, with hazard warning lights on, was parked next to a 'BUSES ONLY' sign! Worse, *my end* of the bay, not the far end. Now he must have had a guilty conscience because I could sense he was trying to escape after seeing me in his rear mirror. That made me swerve so as to miss his front door. Then dead crafty, he'd braked- and left me in the soup. He'd stayed still!

TRUTH : _____ ?

COLLISION NINETY :

A Low-loader turns Left at the end of a Dual Carriageway, with a white van on the inside:

Ken : " I've been in one of these cabs for 23 years: no points on my licence, ever. Other traffic should realize that the empty trailer unit needs dozens of yards to complete a turn : especially the tricky Left turn. That's why we're instructed to have a Left indicator on, even if we have to be in *the Right lane* to achieve the cut. As far as I'm aware, nothing had gone wrong till I was on the ordinary road and White Van raced up behind me, alongside of me, front of me: to make me exchange details. This plumber was forcing me to stop...."

Chris : " A nightmare. Something like Day of the Triffids. Imagine a Colossus forcing you off the road. That's what happened to me - on a Friday when *he* wanted to get home for the weekend. I of all people should know what a peculiar turning-circle he wants. I was a docker! But he was in the Right Lane of the bypass, committed to turning Right - and that's what he should have done. Instead, the more I hooted, the more he ignored me. I even tried to edge back a little, but traffic was too heavy behind me after the first two foot."

TRUTH : _____ ?

COLLISION NINETY-ONE :

A Mini-bus is stalled in the middle lane
of the Motorway, inviting an early collision :

Julia : " It was awful. I was really boxed in on the Motorway at 5pm, in the middle lane. Visibility wasn't bad really. Then a few yards ahead, about 20 yards, I saw this ancient Minibus somewhere it oughtn't to be, like blocking the middle lane. Luckily, I knew to put on my hazard lights as well as braking heavily. I still went into their rear off-side luggage compartment - but damaging metal, not me or them. And there were ever such a lot of them : 11 or twelve, all school-age, arguing or stuffing themselves, or both. They could all have been killed... except most of the cars behind me stopped."

Hussein : "It's a whole new way of driving. The engine gives out whenever it's been idle for a few seconds. So, when I'd taken my foot off the gas - it stalled, in the middle of a move to a faster lane. All before I could raise the alarm. Nothing I could do but pray...."

Divanti : " On our way to the Wedding in Bradford, nothing happened that would get our bus going again. The kids were as good as gold. No panic., We should all have been so happy. And we'd got lots of time..."

TRUTH: _____ ?

COLLISION NINETY-TWO :

A 57-year old man goes round a roundabout at Lunch-time, one September, in Stockport - when the car in front stops

Colin : " I've heard of this happening before - but always thought I'd be smart enough not to get taken in by it. On the quiet short-cut that got me to that particular Roundabout, I was overtaken twice by the same black hatchback with smoked windows. And the front passenger was looking at me peculiar like. Anyway, on the Roundabout itself, what should happen but that this same car slammed on his brakes so I went into his back. And there was no need for him to stop & go mad. Pity the two lads in the back. They were in agony when the Police got to the scene...."

Daley : " This old guy, he couldn't drive for toffee. He'd never been on a Roundabout before. Well, when we had to stop for a pick-up turning right in front of us, behold his car slammed straight into the back of us...."

Earl : " Thank God this pick-up stopped to say what happened. I saw everything too. This old chap looked right nervous, before and after. We didn't stand a chance. Now look at the state of our two mates !"

TRUTH : _____ ?

COLLISION NINETY-THREE :

Car about to turn Right out of Solicitor's Office at 3pm : meets car coming in :

Dawn : " I'd just finished at Wangle, Wrangle & Dongle and was edging across the lowered pavement to turn Right on to Cross Street - when from the other side, the Right-turning gold car, coming *into* Wangles, cut across my bonnet and smashed my offside wing and wing mirror. I've been to that Solicitor before - and, because its car park has a rather narrow gate, you can't do it as fast as him. You've got to do it in two stages like, and slower than him."

Llewellyn : " She seemed all flustered as if texting her boyfriend on her lap. In fact, I thought she was parked up on the pavement. With Wangles sometimes getting full up at peak time. So I signalled Right and gingerly crawled round her into the gateway - when she suddenly came to life. Only looking Right, not Left, she jolted out, as if on to Cross Street - and came to grief. Handy, because Mr. Dongle will be acting for me..."

TRUTH : _____ ?

COLLISION NINETY-FOUR :

One fast hatchback leaves a very large Roundabout into a very minor road by mounting a kerb, then bouncing back to hit two separate cars parking up :

Nev : " Going for an evening run on a Summer evening, I had successfully turned left down the road to the Theatre. I must have been down to about 30mph. at the moment a big ginger cat wandered out in front of my front lights. I was sure I'd killed it, but instead, I took avoiding action, braked, did an untidy U-turn and knocked the sides of these 2 Theatre-goer's cars. These things happen. But there's still a kid's cat supping milk."

Judith: "I'd had to let the other 3 go ahead to the Box Office, and pay - as we were only 10 minutes from Curtain. And the other car - if they did want the Theatre too - was empty. Suddenly, I noticed this bright yellow Super-Mini with spoilers and thumping music. These boy racers meet in the same place every evening, and out-race each other round and round the Roundabout, then out to the Moor and back. They reckon to go 0 to 60 in 10 seconds or less! Anyway, I didn't see any cat or dog. And I was just locking up and getting out my umbrella. So I would have seen anything. No. This driver simply couldn't handle a car so powerful...."

TRUTH _____ **?**

COLLISION NINETY-FIVE:
A Combine-Harvester turns into a farm,
just as it is being overtaken by an Estate :

Young farmer one : " It was my job to jump off of and open the field gate. I did that, then returned to the side of the road to call Corbs in. There was nowt coming, so Corbs began to swing his Harvester enough to get through by me. Only an inch or two to spare. Slow job! Then this guy speeds up, and instead of waiting a mo' for finish, comes by *my* side. Crunch! Big mistake!"

Corbs [Young farmer two] : " Harvester has good mirrors. I checked both sides and saw lane was clear. So I stretched out my Right hand as far as it would go and gently took her through kid's gate. I was barely half way through crossing over when there was an almighty bang, lots of cursing and swearing. Turns out this sales' rep had shot from nowhere and found his passage cut off. Well, I'm quite high up. Bit of bad luck !"

Estate Car Driver : " I'd already sailed through Toxel before nippers came out of school. It was getting a little dark, but not dark enough to hide this dirty great big tractor. So I used my Right indicator and speeded up slightly to get past, just in case anything came downhill faster. Then to my horror, this huge machine loops in front of me! A bit of braking worked...but no way!"
TRUTH : _____

COLLISION NINETY-SIX

A well-loaded car on its way back from B&Q
drifts over on to the wrong side of the road
and is hit by a car from other direction :

Do-it-Yourself Driver : " I couldn't have been more than a mile from pick-up when these 2 old ladies came straight at me as I passed a parked Taxi. In this suburb there's a lot of people parking, so all these 2 old ladies needed to do was *wait* until I'd taken my chance...."

Woman Driver : " It was like a furniture van coming the other way. Timber everywhere, including strapped on the roof. He was meandering *everywhere* !"

Woman Passenger : " I ceased talking to Dora when I saw how busy the road was that Saturday afternoon. Yes, I *did* spot this car with stuff tied on his roof. Though he was swaying, Dora had no reason to stop till *he* was on our side - with *him* not stopping. Shifty fellow!"

Back Seat Passenger of 1ˢᵗ. Car : " I told him not to drive in one go, but to come back for the timber later. I was wedged behind him without paint and cement bags boxing me in. Then he'd put so much clobber in front passenger seat that it all lurched over, migrated, to obscure the front screen and cover a pedal. All the time he was shoving things sideways, I was yelling...."

TRUTH : _____

COLLISION NINETY-SEVEN :
Red car turns Right out of hotel drive in front of a fast-approaching box-van. "Safely" in its chosen far lane, the red car then collides head-on with brown car getting past the van:

Red Car Driver : " I was fortunate in one way, using that road every day to get me to work, always travelling West. Never seen anything like it : there was no way, no way whatsoever, I could have known about the brown car. How stupid for her to pass a van so close to a side turning! Criminal! Better she held on behind, longer."

Box Van Driver : " I was making good progress to my next delivery along that very fast A-road. No bad weather. I must have been doing 55. Nothing prevented my spotting the red car about to come out of that turning. So I slowed a trifle as he was determined to do it. It was a poor call, but quite possible with his acceleration. I must admit I was so busy thinking about the red car, I forgot the *brown* car. Straightway I shouted : O God!"

Helen [Driver of Brown Car] : " Yes, I thought I was dead. I suppose I *did* know cars might emerge from that village - but you can't just dash out regardless. I was within my rights to go ahead overtaking the van. I was going a bit faster, and I always check the road is completely clear. Imagine my surprise! And shock!
TRUTH : _____

COLLISION NINETY-EIGHT :

An economy 4-wheel drive vehicle flipped on to its roof after taking a double bend to access a village: the whole village is set on a hill. Upside down, this vehicle collided with a roadside bench, then glanced a moped before its occupants were got out unharmed.

Moped Rider Arkle : " I was setting out that hot lunchtime. I've never seen an upside-down car before! It was skidding so much far side of the Old Market Place that I hadn't time to dismount. Still thought I was safe! As it happened, neither I nor the bike were much damaged!"

Shopkeeper : "I soon shot out when I heard a woman screaming! And that was a bystander, not the 60year old driver ! I was on my guard in case this Jap 4-wheeler ran into me, but that sturdy bench, *ex-bench*, absorbed 80% of the impact. Only then did I think : <Golly! The moped!> He caught the ricochet - but only on his front wheel. I was more worried the 2 people trapped might catch fire. So dazed -but the tender soon freed them!"

Driver Upside Down : " I'd not done that hill before - and the sun was in my eyes. Dazzling! Pru' was asleep, bless her! so I was able to concentrate on the road. I guess I was doing 30 to 35, ready for the 30 sign - which I'd always do 20 in. Pity it was half-term and this big football rolled out in front of me, which I had to miss..."

TRUTH : _____

COLLISION NINETY-NINE :

At a complex & staggered yellow-box junction in the middle of a large town, three lines of traffic had to negotiate priority. Two drivers both thought they could go : each wanting a conflicting Right turn.

Pedestrian, started & retreated: "I *knew* that road was fatal. They all expect *me* to know what's turning Left behind me while I'm attempting to cross. I do try to make eye contact. To-day three cars plus me needed the same intersection. Two cars crashing shook us all up!"

Driver 'A' turning Right where Pedestrian proceeds: "When I saw this walker gesturing, I held back 5 secs. Then, when I was *certain* the yellow box was mine for the taking, I turned just where the hoodie had feared me *and* the chappie behind him. But I'd only got part way in, when this fool from the one-way system on my Left dashed out to make *his* Right turn, clean across my bows. Maybe the lady behind *me* had signalled to B he could go first....while she was prepared to hold back..."

Driver 'B' turning Right to where 'A' had come from: " I had first call on that Yellow Box. The walker was safe; there was a gap; *and* this lady gestured me to go. So it was mine for the taking. Anybody also turning Right had a duty to give way to me, as I was first, like. Course, I knew there was another car: he wisely *static*."
TRUTH :_____

COLLISION ONE HUNDRED :

A Roundabout beneath the Motorway also carried traffic leaving - or joining - three other roads. And though traffic engineers painted white arrows on each dedicated lane, 2 cars still collided, side-on.

Silver car driver : " I'd been all round the Roundabout once, trying to rejoin the Motorway : but ongoing road-works meant some signs were missing. At last, I found I needed one of the two middle of 5 lanes for Motorway South. So when the lights changed, I was already signalling Right to join my chosen quarter-to-12 lane. And my eyes were scarce leaving the relevant wing-mirror. My heart went to my boots when it dawned upon me the Vauxhall already in the proper lane wasn't going to stop to let me join first. He must have realized we were set on a collision course, but still he ignored me. Anyway, it would have been wrong not to attempt it."

Gold car driver : " You sometimes see it : a driver who has clearly never been on that Roundabout before. Some drivers *are* patient, and anxious to compromise. The *silver* car driver , however, was *not* one to suffer fools gladly - so he probably pushed to get in ahead of me, when he could. Anyway, I *couldn't* let him in :because the car behind me was pressing me to go with the lights. Eventually, the Silver one panicked and lodged in a space there never was, with vision he never had...."
TRUTH : _____

APPENDIX ONE :
WHY DO WITNESS STATEMENTS MATTER ?

*** Road Collisions are never victimless ;

*** At worst, there has been death or serious injury ; better : a party suffers "minor injury" ;

*** Survivors rely on Witnesses: at best impartial;

*** In turn, Survivors will churn over and over in their minds : "What if...?" and "If only..." ;

*** Police investigators are helped if Witnesses stop to insist with enquiries ;

*** Magistrates' and Crown Courts need good Witnesses ;

*** Insurance Companies need those same good Witnesses [Motor Claims come in at billions of pounds per annum];

*** Those actually insured may need a Witness is order to preserve a No Claims' Bonus, to bring down next year's premium, or to avoid paying an Excess on repairs;

*** Points on the Licence/ sometimes the Licence itself can be affected by reliable Witness statements ;

*** Other Witnesses themselves are much heartened by confirmation that what they thought they saw was approximately what they actually saw ;

***All Roadcraft depends on alert observation ;

***All Roadcraft depends on the Feedback Loop.

APPENDIX TWO :
WHY ARE WITNESS STATEMENTS
OFTEN SO IMPERFECT ?

***Each Witness has only a few seconds to digest a collision ;

***Witnesses are often actually within one of the vehicles in collision ; also might have told spouse/parent of different whereabouts; worse might not be supposed to drive that day;

***Witnesses have to preserve their own lives & limbs ;

***Witnesses are frequently on their way to somewhere else, so that obligation is uppermost in their minds ;

***Witnesses rarely have more than half an eye on what is happening ;

***Witnesses must not cause *another* fall or collision by seeking to make sense of the first collision;

***Witnesses might well put First Aid and dialling 999 before recounting what actually took place ;

***Where it is a horror collision, the Witness might be in almost as much shock as one or more of the participants ;

***The Witness or Witnesses might actually know, worse be related to, the alleged culprit ;

***The Collision might be a very long way ahead;

***What the Witness sees is often the Aftermath, not the collision itself ;
***&, finally, the Witness might want to minimize either the evidence *or its importance* - so as not to be delayed.

ΩΨΩΨΩΨΩΨΩ

One of the biggest problems with Witness statements is how few of them there are!

Not many Witnesses stop to recount - or to draw on a piece of paper - what they have seen.

Why interfere? Why lose shopping, drop-off or parking time? Won't be listened to!

Frequently they are *discouraged* from doing so by one of the drivers involved : " Don't worry! We'll sort this out;" or by the Police : " It's all in hand. We shall not be needing you, Madam. Thankyou!"

In fact, "old-fashioned policing" is profoundly out of fashion! Police forces are being pared down to the bones - and "RTAs" are frequent, repetitious, time-consuming....and not "real" detective work.

ΩΨΩΨΩΨΩΨΩΨΩ

APPENDIX THREE :
WHAT DO - OR DO NOT - INSURANCE
COMPANIES TELL PEOPLE TO DO ?

1. Stop !

2. Turn off your engine / perhaps another party's engine too; and use fire extinguisher if one is to hand.

3. Ensure injured parties are rescued, provided that will not *worsen* their injury;

4. All go to a safe place : especially important in darkness, or where traffic is very fast-moving, eg. on the motorway;

5. Only give general information: driver's licence information, insurance agent contact, and anything required by law enforcement or medical professionals to ensure the situation is safe;

6. Do NOT admit fault;

7. Do not confront the other party of the "accident" in an emotional or hostile fashion. Even if you're not at fault, you can still prejudice any auto accident claim by your actions AFTER the "accident;"

8. To get compensation in a vehicle "accident" claim, you must show that your damages were the result of the other

driver's negligence. This can be tricky in cases where a collision has multiple causative factors. (If a police report was made it is likely to carry a lot of weight in settlement negotiations.);

9. Remember, you are under no obligation to call the Police out, provided there has been damage to vehicles only, not to a person or persons or to roadside furniture or a third party's property;

10. 1f you belong to a Rescue Organization, contact them to get you and/or your family and/or your damaged vehicle to the place(s) they ought to be in;

11. Back home, read every clause of your Insurance Policy ;

12. Then collect all documentation into one single file. You will need this file many times.

13. If Police or your Insurance Company will not arrange a full reconstruction of the Collision, ask both to create a reconstruction on screen, using C.G.I.

14. Keep every party on its toes, if necessary petitioning Crown Prosecution Service *yourself*. Because it is in almost everyone's interest - *except your own* - to minimize what's happened and to keep you quiet.

ΩΨΩΨΩΨΩΨΩΨΩΨΩ

APPENDIX FOUR :
A BRIEF INTRODUCTION TO
SENTENCING :

***Uninsured, untaxed, and hit-and-run drivers and riders, by definition, can rarely be *tracked down*, never mind brought to justice;

*** Sentencing is spread over many Courts;

*** Sentencing is uneven across the country;

*** There are many other disposals long before Court : parking ticket, fixed-penalty notice, speed-awareness course, extra Road Craft training, warning, unofficial warning...

principally " NFA" : No Further Action

*** Police are often reluctant to recommend prosecution, even to consider it!

*** The Crown Prosecution Service (CPS) has to be satisfied that the evidence has been collected ; that the evidence is fairly watertight ; and that there is a public interest proceeding towards proceedings;

*** The DVLA isn't always up to speed on its own paperwork, endorsements or disqualifications;

*** Fines imposed are often not collected with rigour and vigour by Magistrates' Courts;

*** Guilty parties disappear abroad ; more likely, back abroad - where they are elusive;

*** Although not officially written into law, Police and the CPS frequently resort to "plea bargaining" : a discussion with Defence as to whether they'd accept: "Death by Careless Driving," instead of "Death by Dangerous Driving" - or "Driving without Due Care and Attention," instead of "Careless Driving" (the logic being far less time in Court) ;
*** Witnesses might not actually appear in Court - so leading to a case being dropped at the last minute;
*** Police might not appear in Court;
*** Victims / Survivors might not have been offered Court preparation ;
*** Victims / Survivors might be too shattered, ill - by Court-date dead - to give compelling evidence;
*** Victims / Survivors might not be able or permitted to give a persuasive "Victim Statement;"
*** Magistrates & Judges might themselves be motorists - or unconsciously sympathetic to truckers;
*** Offending parties might be able to hire the most learned Counsel who have reputations like "Mr. Loophole" (in the extreme) for getting defendants off...or finding holes in Police / Highways' procedure;
*** Juries might "swallow" the Defence;
*** Most important of all, Driver Sentences have been incredibly *lenient*. Life is cheap on the roads. The offender is "remorseful" (?) and "has suffered enough." Even cross-country guidelines are lenient.

APPENDIX FIVE :
VICTIM STATEMENTS :

Victim Statements are far better labelled :
" *Survivor* Statements" - because victimhood is about the last self-advertisement anybody coming through a Road Crash / having been run over / run down / or near miss, would ever *choose*.

Always insist on making a Survivor Statement - whether anybody asks for it or not! Send one to your Solicitor, Police Liaison Officer... and your Insurance Company, with copies for the opposition.

Because the legal system of England & Wales is strictly adversarial; because it views the status of the Survivor as lowly / whining / pathetic indeed ; and because everything depends on what was in the offending Driver's *mind* / purpose / deliberation on the day of the Collision, much depends on the insistence / importuning of the Survivor himself / herself.

If necessary, ask family and friends help you compose and type up your Survivor Statement, including all these issues - if they apply - and in a logical order:

** the shock of death ;
** how you will miss the person/people killed ;
** what the person/people killed would have been or done or achieved or endowed, had they lived ;

119

** the impact of seeing death(s) on the day;
** your own injuries;
** the length of time you will take to recovery;
** partial or permanent disabilities attributable to the Collision ;
** your own mental health subsequent to the Collision;
** shock / trauma / anxiety / sleeplessness subsequent to the Collision ;
** your own employment / unemployment after the Collision ;
** future employment / unemployment / retirement opportunities subsequent to the Collision ;
** your family's shock and loss;
** your family's change of work pattern / shift / advancement at work, following the Collision ;
** loss of leisure, freedom, movement, vacation;
** loss or impairment of day-to-day functions and functioning / self care / housework ;
** loss or damage to a vehicle;
** the effect of having a vehicle not fit to drive ;
** future driving behaviour / confidence / ability to drive...including dread of certain vehicle types / sites ;
**new money worries / disbursements;

FINALLY, & MOST IMPORTANT: INCLUDE A SUMMARY PARAGRAPH ON EVERYTHING THAT HAS CHANGED FROM IMMEDIATELY PRE-COLLISION, TO POST-COLLISION.

ΩΨΩΨΩΨΩΨΩΨΩΨΩ

APPENDIX SIX :
THE RIPPLE EFFECT OF
VEHICLE CRASHES :

<u>one</u> :collision-breath test-disqualification-redundancy

<u>two</u> : collision-disability-divorce-downsize-isolation

<u>three</u>: collision-rubbernecking-second collision-chaos

<u>four</u> : collision-traffic jam-candidate misses interview

<u>five</u> : collision-traffic jam-meeting cancelled-no order

<u>six</u> : collision-damage to barriers-1000s of hours lost

<u>seven</u> :collision-estrangement-homelessness-vagrancy

<u>eight</u> : collision-injury-sporting career abandoned

<u>nine</u> : collision-brain injury-book(s) never written

<u>ten</u> : collision-death-orphan status-going off the rails

<u>eleven</u> : collision-death of partner-no hope of children

<u>twelve</u> : collision-still birth-separation-panic attacks

<u>thirteen</u> : collision-loss of job-loss of home-acute debt

<u>fourteen</u>: collision-depression-underperforming-debt

<u>fifteen</u> : collision-summoned upstairs-sacked-debt

<u>sixteen</u> : collision-loss of car-collision in hired car

<u>seventeen</u> : collision-hand injury-loss of dexterity

<u>eighteen</u> : collision-amputation of leg-immobility

<u>nineteen</u> : collision-sleeplessness-despair-suicide

<u>twenty</u> : collision -four court cases-obsession-despair

<u>twenty-one</u> : collision-loss of car-use taxi-taxi crashes

<u>twenty-two</u> : collision-headaches-bad temper-divorce

<u>twenty-three</u> : collision-3rd.party death-endless guilt

<u>twenty-four</u> : collision-panic-disorientation-collision

B E R E F T

It came upon an August morn
That Mum and she to Hull had gone
And there they shopped till they had done :
Myself so reassured.

It came upon an August morn
That lad did take his motor out
And on the roads did show his clout :
Himself still uninsured ?

It came upon an August Noon
That Police did on my doorbell ring :
" They are bad tidings that we bring..."
Spake they with one accord.

" At Hollym Cross there was a smash
Which did your fam-ly's car involve...
'Twil take some weeks for us to solve :
No one from fate inured."

So now I sit at home bereft :
No spouse or daughter in their chairs...
But matching benches shall be theirs :
For local Church procured.

***

*This Poem was written after its Author arrived early one morning in
a village and sat in the grounds of its distinctive Parish Church.
Only upon standing up and reading the inscriptions carved into that
bench and the one next to it did he realise that two people
had died on exactly the same day in the Year 2000.*

SUGGESTED SOLUTIONS FOR COLLISIONS ONE TO ONE HUNDRED :

Please note : these Solutions can never be conclusive.
The Author is working on the clues he himself
gave & adhered to throughout.
Some readers will rightly use a different set of
assumptions and perspectives.

ONE :FEDCBA; TWO:FDEBAC;THREE:DCABFE;FOUR:FEBADC
FIVE:EACDFB;SIX:ABCDEF;SEVEN:FEDCBA;EIGHT:ECABDF
NINE:FCADBE;TEN:CFDBAE;ELEVEN:DFBECA;TWELVE:BFCABE
THIRTEEN:DCBEFA;FOURTEEN:BCFEAD;FIFTEEN:DCEAFB
SIXTEEN:FBEDAC;SEVENTEEN:ACFBDE;EIGHTEEN:BCFADE
NINETEEN:BFCDEA;TWENTY:FDACBE;TWENTY-ONE:FEBCAD
TWENTY-TWO:EDFABC;TWENTY-THREE:DEBFAC;
TWENTY-FOUR:ACDEBF;TWENTY-FIVE:EDFCBA;
TWENTYSIX:CDAEBF;TWENTY-SEVEN:CDFBAE;
TWENTY-EIGHT:EAFDCB;TWENTY-NINE:DCBFAE;THIRTY:BDFCEA;
THIRTY-ONE:ABFDCE;THIRTY-TWO: ABCFDE;
THIRTY-THREE:CBAEDF;THIRTY-FOUR:DFACEB
THIRTY-FIVE:BCEAFD;THIRTY-SIX:DCFBEA;THIRTY-SEVEN:FCDBEA
THIRTY-EIGHT:ACFDEB;THIRTY-NINE:EDBFCA;FORTY:DAFBEC
FORTY-ONE:FCADEB;FORTY-TWO:CFBADE;FORTY-THREE:ADFCEB
FORTY-FOUR:ECBDAF;FORTY-FIVE:ADBCFE;FORTY-SIX:EDACFB
FORTY-SEVEN:EABFDC;FORTY-EIGHT:CABFDE;
FORTY-NINE:CEFDBA;FIFTY:EBDFAC;FIFTY-ONE:EABDFC
FIFTY-TWO:FDBEAC;FIFTY-THREE:ACEDFB;FIFTY-FOUR:DBACFE;
FIFTY-FIVE:BACDEF;FIFTY-SIX:FEDCBA;FIFTY-SEVEN:ABEFDC;
FIFTY-EIGHT:CFDEBA;FIFTY-NINE:ABCDEF
SIXTY:SOME LONE-VEHICLE COLLISIONS,INTO
TREES,DITCHES,DYKES,UNDERGROWTH,ETC. GENUINELY ARE SEEN
BY NOBODY;WE MAY NEVER KNOW WHY WHEN OTHER LONE-
VEHICLE COLLISIONS ARE *REPORTED BY* NOBODY-MAYBE NOT TO
BE TRACED AT ALL,NOT TO BE TRACED YET,*OR* NOT TO BE TRACED
WHILE UNDER THE INFLUENCE OF DRINK OR DRUGS.

CONTD...

suggested solutions continued......

SIXTY [EXTRA] : CROSS-OVER, DUAL CARRIAGEWAY [BLACK S.U.V]
SIXTY-ONE : LOLLIPOP-MAN KNOCKED DOWN [BY STOLEN CAR]
SIXTY-TWO : THREE CHILD PEDESTRIANS MOWN INTO [VAN]
SIXTY-THREE : ADVERT SEEN FROM HIGHWAY [FLEET DRIVER]
SIXTY-FOUR : FIRE ENGINE JUMPING A 'T' JUNCTION [NOBODY?]
SIXTY-FIVE : PUB CAR PARK FIGHT [CAR ANXIOUS TO LEAVE]
SIXTY-SIX : AIR-SHOW ABOVE AN 'A' ROAD [WOMAN DRIVER,50]
SIXTY-SEVEN : CAR OVER CLIFF WITHOUT SLOWING [THAT DRIVER]
SIXTY-EIGHT : CAR REVERSES DOWN ROAD TO HOUSE [ADVANCER!]
SIXTY-NINE : MOTORCYCLIST UNSEATED [BIKER IN DARK HELMET]
SEVENTY : TRAFFIC-LIGHT FAILURE [SADLY:RIGHT-TURNER]
SEVENTY-ONE : FUNERAL CORTEGE SEVERED [CORTEGE JOINER]
SEVENTY-TWO : VAN TURNING LEFT TRAPS CYCLIST [VAN]
SEVENTY-THREE : CAR REVERSING IN MULTI-STOREY [REVERSER!]
SEVENTY-FOUR : VERY HIGH LORRY, SHORT PEDESTRIAN [NOBODY?]
SEVENTY-FIVE : CAR ROLLS OVER ON STEEP VERGE [MUM DRIVER]
SEVENTY-SIX : DUAL-CARRIAGEWAY OCCUPIED [2ND.CAR JOINING]
SEVENTY-SEVEN : BUS PASSENGER MAROONED IN ROAD [HERSELF]
SEVENTY-EIGHT : STONES,BOTTLES, CHAOS , IN RIOT [RIOTERS]
SEVENTY-NINE : POLICE CHASE SUSPECTED JOYRIDER [POLICE?]
EIGHTY : CAR LEAVES ROAD AFTER NARROW 'Z-'BEND BRIDGE [???]

EIGHTY-ONE : EMILY & KATE'S STORIES RING TRUE
EIGHTY-TWO : SURPRISINGLY, PAUL & ALF TELL TRUTH
EIGHTY-THREE : MARCEL IS PROBABLY RIGHT - & *NOT* ROAD RAGE
EIGHTY-FOUR : THE LORRY DRIVER, AMAZINGLY, RECALLS WELL
EIGHTY-FIVE : BOB & SARA ARE ACCURATE - & ACTED BEST
EIGHTY-SIX : SONIA'S STORY ADDS UP, BORNE OF PATIENCE
EIGHTY-SEVEN : JANE -ABLE BODIED!- TELLING TRUTH
EIGHTY-EIGHT : ADRIAN THE ELDERLY DRIVER : BETTER RECALL
EIGHTY-NINE : PHIL [DRIVER ON A MOBILE] STILL NEEDS BENEFIT
NINETY : KEN : LOW-LOADER DRIVER, POTENTIAL BULLY, IS CLEAR
NINETY-ONE : JULIA GIVES BETTER TESTIMONY THAN MINIBUS
NINETY-TWO : "CRASH-FOR-CASH" ROTTEN TALE; COLIN RELIABLE
NINETY-THREE : DAWN MORE TRUTHFUL *LEAVING* HER SOLICITOR
NINETY-FOUR : JUDITH, IMMERSED IN DRAMA, STICKS TO STORY
NINETY-FIVE : SURPRISINGLY, YOUNG FARMER 'A' - & CORBS
NINETY-SIX : WOMAN DRIVER, HER PASSENGER + *DIY PASSENGER*!
NINETY-SEVEN : BOTH THE BOX-VAN DRIVER *AND HELEN* CORRECT
NINETY-EIGHT : ARKLE AND SHOPKEEPER BOTH RECALLING WELL
NINETY-NINE : PROBABLY BOTH PEDESTRIAN & DRIVER 'B' RIGHT
ONE HUNDRED : THE SILVER CAR DRIVER..........*but choosing is not easy*

SELECT BIBLIOGRAPHY :

There is a surprising shortage of good, modern, literature on Vehicle Collisions - especially for a non-specialist readership: this despite numerous films, plays, novels, short stories and radio broadcasts that rely upon the Vehicle Collision - & Car Crashes - to move a story forward. Worse: despite Vehicle Collisions having an immeasurable impact on nearly every person, of whatever age, in every school, every hospital, every Court of Law, every workplace, every community.

1) Required Publications

Bingham & Berryman's Personal Injury & Motor Claims

Blackstone's Magistrates' Court Handbook

Fleet Management [*Robert & Michelle Currie*]

Know Your Traffic Signs [*Dept. for Transport*]

Motorcycle Roadcraft : The Police Rider's Handbook [*Police Federation*] **KEY**

Observational Before & After Studies in Road Safety : *Highway & Traffic Engineering Measures* [*E. Hauer*]

Pass Your Advanced Driving Test [*I.A.M.*]

Roadcraft : The Police Driver's Handbook [*Police Fedn*]

The Official DVSA Guide to Driving [*DVSA*] **KEY**

The Official Highway Code [*Dept. for Transport*] **KEY**

The *RoSPA* Bicycle Owner's Handbook

The Transport Manager & Operator's Handbook [*David Lowe*]

Victim Support Handbook [*VS + Philippa Spackman*]

2) Other Publications Worth Tracking Down

A Road Safety Workbook for Young Riders [A.Pilgrim]
A Traffic Officer's Companion [Gordon Wilson]
Accident Black Spot [M. Austin] **KEY**
Advanced & Performance Driving [*Reg Local*]
Advanced Motoring [*I.A.M.*]
Back on Track [*Fiona Ford*]
Battle for the Roads of Britain [*Keith Laybourn*]
Car Crime [*Claire Corbett*]
Crash [*J.G. Ballard*]
Death on the Streets [*Robert Davis*]
Death Drive [*Stephen Bayley*]
Highway Engineering [*M. Rogers*]
How to Drive : *the Ultimate Guide* [*Ben Collins*]
Insurance Claim Secrets Revealed [*R.D. Longcore*]
Juggernaut [*John Wardroper*] **KEY**
Let's Go Out : *a Road Safety Activity Book* [*Sigsworth*]
Look Out on the Road [*Humphreys & Ramsay*]
On Roads [*Joe Moran*] **KEY**
Practical Road Safety Auditing [*Belcher & Proctor*]
Road Accidents : Prevent or Punish ? [*J.J. Leeming*]
Sentencing in a Rational Society [*Nigel Walker*]
Sentencing the Motoring Offender [*Roger Hood*]
The Impact of the Motor Car [*Barbara Preston*] **KEY**
Traffic : *Why We Drive the Way We Do* [*T. Vanderbilt*]
Please also read local Police or L. A. Road Safety Unit's literature ;
    & BRAKE and Living Streets' own pamphlets and leaflets .

BROKEN
TRANSPORT....

....or Broken Lives ?

OTHER RECENT BOOKS BY GODFREY HOLMES

THE LINE- STORY
The Nation's Newest Pastime
978-0-9536016-2-2

YOUR CONVERSATION - OR MINE ?
200 Tactics When Talking
978-0-9536016-0-9

A DICTIONARY OF OPPRESSION IN THE WORKPLACE
978-0-9536016-5-3

A DICTIONARY OF TRUANCY
978-0-9536016-6-0

SANDCASTLES DO NOT FALL
New Holderness Verse
978-0-9536016-4-6

STILL STANDING AT FIVE :
A Complete Guide to Relations in the Workplace
978-0-9536016-7-7

TWIXT SCHOOL & DESPAIR :
A Complete Guide to Truancy
978-0-9536016-8-4

all available from Nethermoor Books, telephone : 01964-615258,
or from your Local Bookshop or from Amazon

ΩΨΩΨΩΨΩΨΩ

PRINTED & BOUND BY WARD & PINKNEY [PRINTERS]
WEST 1, NORTHUMBERLAND AVENUE,
KINGSTON-UPON-HULL, EAST YORKSHIRE HU2 0LN
telephone : 01482-325014